SURVIVAL AT WORK & HOME
Saco-Lowell Shops in WW II

SURVIVAL AT WORK & HOME
Saco-Lowell Shops in WW II

By Roy P. Fairfield

For Joe Lewis,
With fond regards
&
Best Wishes,

Roy

12/09

Bastille Books
Saco, Maine

Published by Bastille Books, 371 Main St., Saco, Maine 04072, (207) 282-2653
E-mail: yorfa5@earthlink.net

ISBN: 0-9621921-8-X

Printed in the United States of America.

Photography: front cover, property of Dyer Library Association, used with permission; back cover, © M. Donna Fairfield
Inside: pp. 243–250, property of Dyer Library Association, used with permission

Design, Typography, and Setup: Custom Communications Inc., 11 Wentworth Street, Biddeford, ME 04005, (207) 286-9295, www.desktoppub.com

Dedicated to:

Maryllyn R. Fairfield

M. Donna Fairfield

Jane Fried

Sallie Huot

With Appreciation for Other Assistance:

A. William Kany

Leslie Rounds & Dyer Library Staff

Kitty Ahlquist Chadbourne

Tom Laga, Ph.D., Editor

CONTENTS

DRILL PRESS: *A tall upright machine useful for suddenly snatching flat metal bar stock out of your hands so that it smacks you in the chest and flings your soda pop across the room splattering it against that freshly stained heirloom piece you were drying.*

—Herbert W. Geiler Jr.

SELECTED CHRONOLOGY OF WORLD WAR II

1939 Sept 1   Germany Invades Poland
1940 May 12   Germany Invades France
1941 March 11   Lend-Lease with Britain Begins
      Dec 7   Bombing of Pearl Harbor
1943 Aug 23   Battle of Stalingrad begins
      July 5   Mussolini Overthrown
      Nov 22–Dec 7–1944   Allies' Leaders Meet
1944 Mar 15   Japan Invades India
      June 4   Allies Enter Rome
      June 6   D Day – Allies Land in Normandy
      Sept 14   British Enter Athens, Greece
      Nov 7   FDR Wins a Fourth Term
1945 Jan 16   Battle of Bulge Ends
      Feb 3–4   Firebombing of Dresden, Germany
      Feb 19   Battle of Iwo Jima
      April 12   FDR Dies; Harry Truman Becomes
                  President
      May 7   Victory / Europe (VE - Day)
      July 16   First Atomic Bomb is Exploded
      Aug 6–8   Atomic Bombing of Hiroshima & Nagasaki
      Aug 14   Japan Surrenders (V-J Day)
      Sept 2   Formal Surrender on Battleship, Tokyo Bay

Source: Time-Life Books, *Second World War*. NY, 1989

PREFACE

When agreeing to participate in an historical society panel on the textile industry in the Winter of 2007, I searched long and hard for a brief but comprehensive story about the Saco- Lowell Shops, the textile machinery manufacturer for which I worked for sixty-six months between 1936 and 1944 (between high and graduate schools). I was aware, of course, of the monumental history by George Sweet Gibb, *The Saco-Lowell Shops: Textile Machinery Building in New England, 1813–1949* (Cambridge, Harvard University Press, 1950). I had consumed that volume with great enthusiasm and insights while doing my doctoral thesis for Harvard, a document which I modified for lay consumption into the book, *Sands, Spindles and Steeples* (Portland, House of Falmouth, 1956).

So my challenge was to write a volume that not only caught the challenge of a company that had experienced several mutations in more than a century of manufacturing and textile production. Saco-Lowell became a name symbolizing the revolutionary challenges of design and the ups and downs of survival in a field of fairly modest profits after some losses. Also, I felt that it was important to put the technical problems into ordinary language, give readers a sense of the nature of production in the variety of departments. Too, I wanted to discuss some of the vital social and demographic issues growing out of manufacturing in Saco and Biddeford as communities.

When facing these several issues, I finally decided to make the company live by writing in the context of an important experience that I had at Saco-Lowell during World War II when the company's survival was alleged to pivot around a program in which I would serve as "point man" via a Cost Analysis of nineteen representative machines; the analysis was designed to convince the Office of Price Administration in Washington, D.C. that their frozen prices/costs on labor and materials decrees might kill the company when it ceased wartime production and resumed domestic (ie. textile machinery) manufacturing.

When I began the writing, I had a fairly clear structure for the volume. Because I'd always held a position, albeit it an office wherein I had interaction with the manufacturing departments, I had a fairly comprehensive knowledge of the twenty-plus departments. In short I knew the geography of the shops, had a fairly good knowledge and rapport with the foremen and other leaders in the company. While my background was not in textile technology, I did grow up in a garage, knew the fundamental elements and uses of machinery, had handled a great variety of tools and earlier in the war when I'd helped expedite in-coming equipment for setting up the manufacture of bogey wheels for Ford Motor Company's Bren Gun Carrier. If the position I was to assume had been open for potential applicants, I doubt that I would have applied for it. Furthermore, I had already been admitted to graduate school, and in my heart and with family support, I wanted to see that through.

As I began the tasks, I could not have imagined the kind and dimensions of issues that arose in that Summer of 1944. Also, as I felt my way toward facing the challenges of the tasks, the problems and the opportunities changed, sometimes daily. Not only did I need to learn more about cost analysis, also had to learn how to resolve personnel issues which I could never have imagined or even prepared for. That is what made writing the account such a challenge.

As I progressed with the analysis and story, however, I realized that I would have to invent dialogue that conveyed many realistic situations. I have facetiously admitted to friends and associates, "When I ran out of facts, I invented them!" In short, the book has some elements of historical fiction; yet, I think that the result is one that fairly accurately conveys the nature of the Company and its mission. While the Company was manufacturing war products in the Summer of 1944, the Project led to the relief the company needed in establishing its prices following V Days, 1945.

Also invented: all proper names except for Grace [Bennett], Priscilla [Fairfield Ladd Knight], Mark Black, R.A. Kettley, David Edwards, A.V. Stuart. My intent: embarrass nobody.

Any errors of fact or fantasy are mine alone. I am indebted to Dyer Library and its staff for access to documents and photographs. One textual clarification: when I refer to the Saco-Lowell Shops in a corporate sense, I normally use the upper case (Shop); when I refer to the physical facilities in the singular or plural senses, I use lower case (shop or shops).

One other explanation: while I was tempted to intersperse photos with the text, it seemed better to add them as a group in the end materials. See page 243 for the guide through those insights; or, with access to Dyer Library, ask to see some of the Saco-Lowell pamphlets or handbooks to specific machines.

Roy P. Fairfield
February 2009

1. THE COST PROJECT–DILEMMA

It was early May, 1944. I was working in the tool crib of the Bendix Aviation subcontract job where the Saco-Lowell Shops made anti-aircraft gun controls. The tactics and strategy of the War flow seemed to be moving from defensive to offensive. Hence, fewer anti-aircraft guns were needed. Meanwhile, in light of the original orders, the Shops had ordered a certain number of tools, such as 3/4″ high- speed twist drills, and other such tools necessary to produce the units on order. So somebody had to do the manual work of allocating the proper number for the future, but setting aside the number required when renegotiating contracts with Army Ordinance. It was tedious work; yet, those of us in the Terminations Department who had been employed a year or so making such cuts under the direction of both the technical and purchasing supervisors, worked at the task not only in identifying the "surplus" tools in the various Shop departments but also moving these tools physically to that Department on Pearl Street, Biddeford, one of the former Pepperell buildings.

For a year or so before I had been in charge of that operation because I had a fairly comprehensive knowledge of the entire Shop, having gone directly there upon graduating from Thornton Academy in 1936. In fact, my first job was as "runner boy," taking two daily hikes of five miles each changing techni-

1

cal data on Specification Sheets and Parts Lists from which machinery was built. Following that I'd served as file clerk, Chair of a one-person Contracts Department where comparing lists and selling prices and was part of the comptroller process that "happened" at the President's office in Boston. Then during my Bates College years, I worked on many different projects during summers, vacations and week ends as my family and I cobbled together enough money to pay for tuition. In December, 1942, my final semester at Bates, my Saco-Lowell supervisor petitioned the Bates Dean and Faculty for me to truncate my final year by a few weeks in order to be present when Saco-Lowell started to fulfill a contract to make bogey wheels (the undercarriage) for Army Bren Gun Carriers being manufactured by Ford Motor Company. The petition was granted. Helping set up that contract, I worked with the expediting of tools, jigs, fixtures, etc. while starting the job. At that time I was being changed so frequently from one draft status to another that it made my head swim. What next?

The phone call which I received while counting twist drills in the Bendix Corporation Job's Tool Crib was a dramatic event following a traumatic decision to escape the indecision of being drafted by the Army where I was 1-A, being admitted to Phi Beta Kappa's Naval program to learn Japanese at the University of Colorado. I was evicted from that program for physical and "mental" reasons (I asked too many questions!), returned to Maine to be rated as 4-F. I then applied and was admitted to the Harvard Graduate School of Arts and Sciences planning to enter late that October. In the interim I planned on returning to Saco-Lowell's Termination Department to work under the supervision of Harry Sawyer, one of my former Thornton teachers. Only two months before he worked under my supervision! The situation felt strange.

So the vital and somewhat traumatic phone call to the tool crib came in from Mark Black, the department Chair for whom I had worked most of my Saco-Lowell days. Upon returning from my ill-fated Naval venture in Colorado, he had assured me, though somewhat vaguely, "We are planning a program in which you'll be involved." So this phone call was a response to his promise.

He exclaimed, "Get over to my office immediately. We have an appointment with Vice President Kettley in fifteen minutes!"

My heart raced, for I had seen this man, corporate VP as well CEO of local Shops operations, many times during my 66-month association with the company. Also, I shared a common shops perception that he was a rather distant and cold person. This was reinforced by the fact that he lived in a house surrounded by a wall on an up-scale Saco street. But, feel as I might, I walked briskly through the foundry yard where the crane pulleys in the long crane and magnet over the metal scrap pile were whinnying their way to the molten pit of the blast furnaces. Breathless, I rushed into Mark Black's office. And within minutes Mark and I were facing the CEO in his office.

Kettley began by affirming that Black was recommending me to do a very complex but important job. In essence he began by saying, "Roy, we're possibly in serious trouble, even facing a crisis. We need a cost analysis to account for the increased material and labor prices that the war has produced. We need to compile the history of manufacturing costs as they stood before the war began; we need it for a representative number of machines in our total product so we don't go under by using old prices as we re-start peacetime production. Before we experience a crisis, we need to approach the U.S. Office of Price Administration (OPA), which has frozen our prices, and present them with a cost analysis reflecting the story of the increases related to both

3

material and labor to produce our textile machines. We must appeal for an increase and hope we are successful in making our case in order to survive."

I spoke up, "Where's the Cost Department in all this?"

Kettley responded quickly, "I told them what we needed. They told me that it would take five years to do it. I told them that they would have no jobs in five years unless we acted now!"

"So what do you propose to do?" I queried.

Kettley opined, "I think we need to act quickly and have answers by the end of this year. We need a new and (for us) a somewhat different approach and this is where you come in. We need to develop a plan wherein we import enough mechanical engineers, maybe one for each department, who will be based in the shops and will analyze each part, each assembly of parts, the materials and labor in each part for as many machines as are representative. Possibly we can use some of the Bedaux (time study) materials, but I think we need to go beyond those records and use these engineers' know-how to get an up-date on those machines. We are counting on the government's Price Administration recognizing the engineers' specializations and reputations to verify what we've done and will have to do when we move from wartime to peacetime production. And we need to do it before the end of this year.

"We are sure to run into resistance. Shop foremen are used to being in charge of their little domains and not used to having "outsiders" looking over their shoulders. They will resent anybody seen as "outsiders." But I will demand that the superintendents of both Biddeford and Saco Divisions of the local shops meet with all of their shop foremen assembled at one time and make it clear that they'll keep their jobs only if they cooperate. I expect you to be at those meetings."

4

I may have expressed thanks for Kettley's and Mark Black's confidence in me. But when I left the CEO's office, my head was swimming. I told Black what he already knew, that I was entering graduate school at Harvard in late October [1944]. He assured me that that was all right, that we might have the job done by then. Also, he said he wanted to discuss my future at Saco-Lowell at some later time . . . as he had before I left for Bates when he tried to talk me out of enrolling because, as he put it, "You would have a great future at Saco-Lowell."

We then got down to the nitty-gritty of planning, how we could organize a special group of people as a means of coordinating work with the foremen and how we would assemble blueprints for each part to the specifications and full lists of parts for each machine. We agreed on the number and identity of representative machines and a back-up staff to handle secretarial and computational processes, tying where possible each part to a specific machine, obtaining information on the types and costs of material for each machine, and so on ad infinitum.

Black also assumed the responsibilities of locating qualified mechanical engineers through a labor broker, this being necessary because of the tight supply of highly specialized engineers although he had a hunch that the war's change of direction, from defensive to offensive, might be freeing up the supply of engineers a bit and this hunch had grown from his preliminary phone calls to potential suppliers. It was now mid-May so we couldn't bring them on location much before mid-June . . . but that I was to start immediately. He also said that Harry Sawyer of our Terminations Department, "would certainly understand the need for immediate action." He'd already apprised Harry of that possibility. Too, he had formed a committee of Saco-Lowell engineers as a screening committee to review the visiting engineers' credentials; he and Kettley would also serve on that committee because the process included drawing up contracts for their work. I told Black that I was glad that he was attending to those details because I didn't feel competent to do so in view of the time bind.

2. MARK BLACK

At the time Mark Black, a man in his fifties and veteran of some two decades in the company, summoned me to join him in Vice President Kettley's office, I'd known him for nearly eight years. He had hired me for my first job the week after my Thornton graduation. Over the years he had not only been my boss, but he served as an informal mentor. Although I had defied his recommendation that I *not* go to college (but stay at Saco-Lowell), he still treated me kindly and hired me summers, vacations, week-ends over the years and was central to "drafting" me into industry a month before I graduated from Bates College. Mark was reared in the Scotch tradition even as he and his siblings worked in the textile industry. He was essentially conservative and would become a trustee at the local bank as well as treasurer of the York Institute in Saco.

When we left the CEO's office and continued our discussion of the project, we discussed frankly what the stakes were to be successful in this project. He had worked and studied diligently in working his way up to top management at the Saco-Lowell Shops. He knew both the pitfalls and the opportunities in the company. I inferred from what he said that I'd better be successful in doing the cost project so that his own reputation be maintained and/or enhanced.

When we reached the nitty-gritty details, he was most helpful in guiding me through some of the stickiest problems, whether we were setting up the physical office, choosing persons to create a support staff or becoming better acquainted with some of the most important power brokers in the company. I needed access to both information and insight. Also, I needed to deal with the Cost Department which was being by-passed to launch the project. Fortunately, I knew some of the members of that department, especially the top man. My sixty-six month stint at the Shops, especially those jobs taking me into almost every department in the company had enabled me to become acquainted with many of the shop foremen and second-hands (assistant foremen). Also, since I had been in charge of the Contract Department, making comparisons between lists and selling prices of the full range of Saco-Lowell textile machines, also grounded me in the nature of the machines that we would cost out. In short, Mark Black was there for both technical and friendly counsel. I appreciated his willingness to accept my decision to return to graduate school and work toward a college professor's position . . . even if he continued to hold out the bait of status and a future at Saco-Lowell.

One of the hopes that I held rather quietly at the time: a desire to interview people from all branches and processes of the company, not only to understand better what accounted for its failures and successes but also to understand people, manufacturing, engineering and company policies and procedures. Also, having been reared in a "family" of carpenters, mechanics, electricians, seamstresses, clerks, and others who used their hands to create and repair "things," I wanted to search more deeply into their attitudes, fears and hopes associated with machine-making. What was it like to work day after day to make a living in physical contexts that I did not as yet understand?

Doing such inquiring while working on this project would

be personally important in my long-term goals to be a professor and possibly a writer. I have to confess that I was not immediately up-front with a means to take these "snapshots." But eventually I shared these privately-held plans with Mark Black. When I first broached the issues with him, he was not too encouraging; but, the more we talked about it and I suggested the informal interviewing technique, he saw no conflict of interest. And so long as I kept my focus on the objective of the project, he saw no difficulty although he admitted that I'd need a good memory to take in all this landscape as well as take notes. He also suggested that we *not* share this "underground" plan with V.P. Kettley. After all, the CEO was an accountant by training and occupation so probably could care less what human factors made the company tick, beyond individual worker's ambitions to make a living, get promotions, salary increments, etc. He offered to assist if I encountered insurmountable obstacles. So I began.

3. INSIDE & OUTSIDE PRESSURES

Creating our Cost Project Office was not difficult. An unused space in one of the original mill sites, currently used as a demonstration of several Saco-Lowell machines, was petitioned off from common spaces. But it was on the same floor as Blueprint Reproduction, Tool Design, List and Specifications Departments and Drafting Room, the personnel of which I knew quite well from six years of contacts. It was on the sunny side of the building, a little warm, but pleasant, without A/C but few departments in the entire factory had air conditioning anyway. Most Mainers knew that anybody requesting A/C were usually told, "If you're too warm, open the windows!"

Mark Black was very helpful in finding able personnel, with shops experience, and that helped. My secretary, Grace, was a very mature woman in her fifties, a stabilizing force; likewise, my sister, Priscilla, in her early twenties, had worked in several departments on that floor but especially in the Reproduction Department where she could prepare the necessary blueprints, parts lists and other documents we needed to carry into the shops for fundamental research. We also had the latest models of Frieden calculators for which we would have progressive need when the data began flowing in from the shops. One fairly elderly man was comfortable at a calculator having had considerable experience figuring costs on parts made from

10

steel bars. Unfortunately, he died of a heart attack before we got too far, but the successor's background is a story in itself . . . as we shall see.

During the first three weeks on this Cost Project, I began working sixty (60) hours a week. I not only had to learn more about cost analysis, via the Cost Department staff and Bedaux (time-study) personnel, but I also attended shop meetings of the department foremen who had had their warning to be cooperative . . . or else! The junior superintendent, the assistant covering the Saco departments, and the senior one those in Biddeford, spelled out in no uncertain terms the importance of the project and the imperative need for *total* cooperation. Surely, nobody could miss the message; their careers and lives depended upon it. My entrée to the Senior Superintendent, whom I did not know too well before the Project began, was enhanced by the fact that his assistant was one of my Thornton classmates. Also, I visited for a round or two with each of the other twenty-plus foremen and their second-hands in command.

Finally, one of the most difficult of the unknowns was Mark Black's task of contacting labor brokers to employ certified engineers. This was a point where we had to use a certain amount of trust in the company through which we went. I knew nothing about the engineering certification process and I don't think that my bosses knew much more. But we began to get resumes of these men who were just finishing such war jobs as setting up the Curtis Wright engines for military planes, inventors of such projects as designing tools for Liberty Ship propellers, and so on. Here, Mark and the Screening committee "did their thing." At the outset , we planned to employ twenty-four mechanical engineers "at the max "so as to have approximately one per department, and to bring them in four at a time so as *not* to alarm the shop foremen too much too quickly. It was my task to assign them to the shop departments, depending upon their skills and the specialty of those departments.

Aside: at the end of three weeks and the week end prior to the first group's arrival, I suddenly came down with a severe case of laryngitis. Ordinarily, I wouldn't have paid it much heed, but I was well prepared to spend whatever time it took to orient the engineers to the Shops, its history and the nature of the production in each department. The laryngitis hit me fairly quickly and *hard*, but it was no wonder in view of the fact that I'd been talking for 40-60 hours a week in many different places and under conditions where the air was badly polluted. When I finally visited my family doctor, Laura Black Stickney (Saco's first female MD but no relation to Mark!), she recommended warm-to-hot lemonade; but, after she'd made the diagnosis and prescription, she looked at me somewhat wistfully and said, "Really for a few days, Roy, you'll really need to shut up!" Normally, I would have protested and continued talking! That was my nature and for years my mother and father had asked, "Roy, must you always have the last word?" But this time I listened and obeyed.

By Monday I felt a little better, but hardly prepared to meet the new (and very expensive!) mechanical engineers. Fortunately for me, we had only four in the first wave; and, fortunately, too, our secretary, Grace, and my sister Priscilla were well prepared to carry some of the load that I would have normally taken. So I was relatively quiet for half a day, then I accompanied them on a tour of the shops on the second day after their arrival. On the third day I accompanied them to their specific departments along with the prepared documents. Hence I loaned each a hand as they began.

The basic objective or premise of this project was both simple and complex. We had prepared work sheets, lists of parts and blueprints for each of the parts under scrutiny. As I recall, we had chosen the first machines to be those with fewer parts and were made in the fewest departments. So it was the task of the engineers to go into the particular departments, work with the foreman and second-hand to locate the particular machines on which the parts would normally be created. A major handicap: these machines were *not* necessarily in production, *but* there might be repair parts in process. So finding the right jigs and fixtures, using what records (including Bedaux's time-study records they could find), using the memories of foremen, second-hands, tool crib managers, etc. the engineer would determine what steps (operations) the part would normally need. We told the engineers repeatedly: *You are here to write history* and *not* recommend new processes for doing the old parts. As we'll see later, this was not easy for the engineers; most of them had just been working on major problems under military contracts; it was one thing to propose and execute new designs for a Curtiss Wright engine used in fighter planes, but quite another to reconstruct processes for a heart cam to go on a spinning frame. If we spelled this out once, we must have repeated it ten times for some of the engineers; they preferred the challenges of new designs over writing the history of Part No. 237 in Department 21 . . . or whatever! (In retrospect this related to changes of which S-L-S was guilty; namely, in not updating its machinery decade after decade or moving it between physical plants when consolidating.)

Although I did not always know the engineers' language, I learned rather quickly and easily how to communicate with most of them. As we'll see in a moment, sometimes human relations became more important than knowledge and skills. Yet, as a Project we were committed to doing history to prove that our current scale of material and labor costs would not bear up

13

under projected post-war production of textile equipment.

But despite all of these handicaps, a personal problem arose fairly quickly. When I received my pay after the first week, I opened my envelope and found $10 less cash than I'd received at my pre-Project job. How come? I immediately went to Mark Black whose investigation led to the revelation: I was being paid at the base rate of persons working as foremen; any overtime that they worked was free to the Shops. Obviously, I could not accept that because I'd made it clear to Black that I was saving money for graduate school, my wife, Maryllyn, had returned to nursing duties at the local hospital, and her mother was caring for our daughter, Donna, now two. Mark declared it a mistake and arranged for me to get paid time and a half for the hours over forty hours (70 hours), a norm for most employees.

Actually, even this was a bit difficult to take psychological-ly in view of the fact that the engineers were paid both salary and living expenses or about $225/week, almost triple my pay; I knew that because I had to sign their verification forms for the Payroll Department. But a question now arose: how would I be able to do interviews and/or begin to get a more comprehensive picture of the shops?

The Larger View
Actually, even the preparation for launching this project provid-ed a quantum leap for better understanding of the Total Shops view, both retrospectively and prospectively. While working at S-L-S, I'd always held an office job requiring knowledge of the textile machines as well as the paper trails for getting the parts made and assembled, both on the erecting floor where each order of machines had at least one representative machine pre-assembled and running before the total order was boxed and shipped. As noted earlier, when first at Saco-Lowell I was a

"runner boy," circulating through the departments twice or approximately ten miles per day. While I engaged in conversation with men and women on every level of competence and authority, I rarely dilly-dallied because there was always work for me to do "back at the office." So in addition to talking with new people, I returned to my recollections of specific persons even as I expanded my acquaintances. Also, I continued to keep a journal of sorts to which I might return for new insights.

More Background
Somewhere about the second week of the first engineers' arrival, several asked if I would tell them more about Saco-Lowell's history and the principal functions the machines performed. So we took a couple of hours on each of two mornings for mini-lectures, questions and answers.

I put the Shops into historical perspective by resorting to the corporate evolution of the old Iron Works that began making nails in 1811 which led to the first use of the Saco River for industrial manufacturing . . . although local saw mills had operated for nearly two centuries. Then came cotton textile machines in a five-story building at the foot of Factory Island . . . how that burned, leading to the founding of York Manufacturing Company in 1831 by a group of Boston investors. The next major step was the founding of a Saco Water Power Company that managed both manufacture of some of the elementary machinery which Lowell, Mass companies had pioneered; add to that the harnessing of water flow (power) and land development.

Also at that time I drew upon three or four of the draftsmen and research engineers who spoke of their own contributions to the revolution that was underway in the textile industry which they hoped would lead to line production and reduce labor costs. In each instance I asked the Saco-Lowell experts to fit their

15

own specific skills into the context of handling the flow of materials from opening the cotton bales to the cleansing of the cotton, laying cotton fiber into parallel skeins via the carding machines to the development of rope-like cotton slivers and on into a variety of warp and woof threads which eventually became cloth via the looms. I asked Saco-Lowell experts to present the big picture rather than getting hung up on details which might bog down the process of gaining a comprehensive picture. To handle any loose ends, figuratively speaking, the draftsmen and research engineers availed themselves to answer further questions and be available to confer if any of the Cost Project engineers wanted further insights.

Also, Grace and I made arrangements for our special engineers to visit the nearby cotton-based Pepperell mills for further, first-hand information or further commentary; at least three of the men took advantage of that opportunity. In short, the four-hours of such effort was a once-over-lightly effort, but all those engineers who'd arrived expressed appreciation for the insights.

The Saco-Lowell Library was also filled with a variety of manuals on specific machines and their evolution at Saco-Lowell's various plants at various times in their 100-year history. When they were reading the manuals, I urged them to note how the company itself described the shortcomings of each machine and what the company was doing to overcome those limitations via research and development. In other words, I encouraged them to partake in the dynamics of textile machine production even as they focused upon history and they were encouraged *not* to stray too far into recommending changes in our current mode of production. I wanted them to catch the big picture without getting lost in the details of their cost project focus.

In many ways it was unfortunate we were doing this analysis decades prior to the evolution of highly readable books on the topic, especially detailed analyses such as George Gibb's *Saco Lowell* (1950) and Steve Dunwell's *The Run of the Mill*. Too, a trip to the Lowell Textile Park in Lowell, Massachusetts might have been enlightening for those wishing to explore the subject further. But, this is also a disadvantage of hindsight.

4. OLD FRIENDS AND NEW

Within a few weeks of launching we had the project in full
motion; first we had four, then eight, then twelve and decided to
stop at sixteen engineers. One of the latter dropped out because
he wanted to work in a larger city and on a more challenging
project. So finally, by mid-July we had fifteen at work in the twenty-plus departments of the manufacturing plant. Although each
day found us wrestling with some kind of minor snag, the parts
forms were filling with data and the office side of the process was
moving along smoothly. Grace and Priscilla were really doing
excellent work. So with the project going well, one morning I
decided to visit some of my old friends in the List-Specifications
Department, just around the corner from our operation.

Ralph Perry
I began with Ralph because he had been the first to welcome me
eight years before when I was fresh from Thornton Academy
and "still wet behind the ears!" Also, we had met times before
when he brought his car to dad's garage a-mornings and I drove
him to work so dad could have the day to do Ralph's repairs. He
took me aside, went over the list of twelve to fifteen employees
in the List and Specs Departments, described their idiosyn-
crasies, touchy topics and essential skills. It was a helpful start,
and I learned the protocol well, learned who were coupled up,

18

who were married, who were probably gays but still in their own special closet. Ralph and I sat beside one another in the Specs Department after he replaced "Ole Perce," when the old veteran succumbed to heart disease; we shared jokes, family issues, etc. When the Shops cut back to a four-day work-week during the 1938 Recession, I offered to take my day off on Wednesdays so Ralph could have a week ends with a seemingly dysfunctional family (for lack of communication).

Also, the two of us schemed practical jokes. For instance, Dicky Prince, a shop foreman, insisted upon explaining away his mistakes with the expression, "You can't make a silk purse out of a sow's ear." When Ralph and I tired of Dicky's excuse for his errors, we found a sow's ear somewhere and snuck it into the Inter Office mail. When Dicky suspected us and asked us point blank if we had done it, we conjured up a way to take him off our trail and deflect his questions without really lying. We asked Dicky how big the sow's ear was. How old did he think it was? When he called one day to say he'd bought a small refrigerator to put the ear in and would show it to us if we wanted to take a stroll to his office some day, we promised to come look, but never did.

Upon another occasion, when "Ole Perce" sat in the chair which Ralph eventually occupied (and used his extensive knowledge of 1870 spinning and roving machines to survive), Ralph highlighted one of Perce's habits of smoking cigars and letting his head fall forward on his desk to burn holes right through whatever paper he was using. (He had apnea.) It was a wonder Ole Perce didn't set himself afire.

Well, while Perce was at lunch one day, Ralph shaped a cardboard face with a large mouth in which he stuck eight to ten cigar stubs and set up the face so it would be staring at Perce when he returned to his desk. In many ways, it was a cruel joke

19

because Perce's medical condition was beyond his control. But when he came waddling in after lunch at 1:12 (he was rarely on time!), Ralph and I were busy at our desks and watching obliquely to see what Perce's reactions might be. He came in, pulled his belt up over his big belly (he was five-foot four in height and four-foot five in circumference), shoved himself into his squeaky swivel chair and stared at the face and the used cigars. Without saying a word, he turned in his chair facing his office mates and grinned an exaggerated grin!

On the occasion of my first visit with Ralph to talk about the Cost Project, he merely said, "I don't know much except that you're the chief of it." He thought that Mark Black had made "a good choice." There was some buzz in the department because Priscilla was running in and out checking on part numbers and making blueprints. He went on to say that some of the senior members of the List and Spec Departments were a bit critical of what was happening, but they pitied me trying to get information out of some of the shop foremen. "But," he added, "most of these folk wouldn't go into the shop for fear of getting dirty; and the women are frequently bitching about getting cast iron dust in their hair when they simply pass the door of the Snagging Room and sometimes even take a long way around that room to reach the time clock via another entrance.

Also, Roy, they know that you are one of the few people around who have a comprehensive view of the shops. It's fortunate that you've not made enemies out there. As for sharp criticism, one of the guys said, and I quote, 'Roy could burn his ass off going thru the foundry when they're pouring red hot cast iron. I wouldn't do it for a farm Down East.'"

Since my self-set fifteen-minute quota per department visit was up, I ambled back to the Cost Project after thanking my old friend for "passing the time of day."

Charlie Crogan

It so happened that only the day before my trek to Specs, I had hired a fellow, Charlie Crogan, to replace the man who had died the previous week, the man with experience figuring costs of cold roll steel parts. As I strode through the office door, I could see that Charlie was scowling and wore a puzzled look. Before returning to my desk, I stopped and leaned against his desk where the Frieden calculator was humming and asked, "Is there something wrong, Charlie?" He looked up, was a bit defensive and commented, "I know you spent half a day with me yesterday, but I can't seem to coordinate my eyes and the machine." I didn't know him very well; yet, I could see that he was pretty "up tight," so I resorted to a baseball cliché!

"Well, as you know, you can't hit a home run every time at bat! Say, do you like baseball, Charlie?"

He looked up through his rather thick glasses, smiled and remarked, "Yeah, I once played for the New York Yankees!"

I was jolted because I'd been a Yankee and Red Sox fan all my life and exclaimed, "You *did*? What position did you play?" Again he smiled and told me his story.

"Yeah, I played for Portsmouth High School and as a senior I hit .400 and knocked out 25 home runs, so the Yankees took me in. I played one year for their Newark farm team, did so well they brought me up for Spring training. That went so well I began the year at Yankee Stadium."

"But, Charlie, I never saw your name in the line-up and I read it everyday!"

Charlie continued with his story. "Well, Roy, one day in April during batting practice before the game, I was behind the pitchers' mound shagging balls, you know, catching them from the outfielders and feeding them to the pitcher. Suddenly, I heard the pitcher scream, 'Look out!' I ducked and quickly put up my gloved hand, full of balls, and caught a line drive right in the middle of those balls and it broke every bone in my hand. I went to the hospital (he held out his left hand, full of scars) and for weeks and months the medics tried to help me. But I could never grip a bat again."

I was, of course, almost in shock because I never expected to have an ex-New York Yankee working with me! We got back to the subject of his figuring parts prices, had an amiable relationship all summer; I even met his family in Buxton one evening. After the Cost Project ended, he took a job in an up-river electrical power plant. We corresponded for several years; but I've never forgotten his response to my question. "Do you like baseball?"

The Cost Project Moves On
While the mechanical engineers were pleasant, they seemed to talk freely among themselves. Although they had come directly from some of the largest and most sensitive war jobs from various parts of the country, I was careful to keep my distance and not become overly friendly with them. Whenever a question arose regarding our processes and its parameters, I had no difficulty communicating with them directly. I had no engineering in my background, but I'd lived around machinery and tools most of my life since my dad ran a garage, constantly had some kind of building project in process and I knew much of the lingo of the textile world after five-plus years working at Saco-Lowell.

I did get a sense of the worlds in which many of our imported engineers lived, and got some odd comments about what it was like to move from major cities like New York, Detroit and Philadelphia to what they called "rinky-dinky" towns like Biddeford and Saco. Some complained, too, that there were "no good restaurants here." Yet they were complimentary about the friendliness of local people, even as they attempted to master the Maine "ayuh" and other unique Maine accents! Few seemed to understand or care for the Franco lingo and were puzzled about the potato being called "potat" rather than "pomme de terre."

They claimed to tune into Radio Station WIDE to catch localisms then mock the announcers' handling of the French language.

But early on a Monday morning a week or so after we released the engineers into the various departments, I received an alarm call from Al Calligan foreman of the Gear Cutting Department. It came only a half hour after the engineers checked in then disappeared into the shop. Al was livid, fairly screamed into the phone, "Roy, get over here and get over here fast!"

I walked as fast as my legs would take me, nearly got run over by one of the little tractors that hauled stuff around the multi-acred plant. I hustled up the stairs to the third floor rather than waiting for the elevator. As I entered Al's glassed-in office on the Gear Job, I saw that not only was Al and the engineer, George Lincoln Spielman present, but also Jim Crosby, the Senior Superintendent of the whole Biddeford "shebang." I said good morning to Al, Jim and George, then asked casually, "What's the matter?"

Al began, "Look, Roy, George here keeps telling us that our methods are obsolete and we ought to do this and we ought to do that! Goddamn-it! Those guys are here to write history. Jim told us that! Can't you get his stinking Jewish fingers out of our machines?"

I was dumb-founded; this was more than a mechanical issue. I spoke quietly to Jim. "I know that you know that I gave each of these visiting experts strict instructions about this. Furthermore this is not a matter of religion or faith, this is a matter of using the information and tools we have to dig out the data we need."

Then I looked at George, whom I had come to like after he told me that his father was a diplomat in pre-war Germany, and had lived much of his early life in Berlin and barely escaped The Holocaust. I said, "George, you'll confirm, will you not, why you're here?"

Very quietly, George said, quite bluntly, "Yes, and I can take Al's anti-Semitism. I've faced it all my life. Ask him if he wants me to leave."

Al then spoke again, but more softly. "Jim, I heard you tell us foremen that we could cooperate or be looking for another job." He was almost in tears when he went on to say, "As you know, Jim, I got my college and engineering training long ago and I've been in charge of this department for more than twenty years. I am not ready to leave." He came up with a half-smile and patted Jim on the knee even as he spoke.

Jim kept his cool. "OK, Al, do we agree that the big problem is George's telling you how to use more sophisticated methods to make your gears?"

"Yes," Al replied, resignedly.

"OK, and George, we know that you may not agree with our methods, but can you do the job you're hired to do in this department?"

"I think so, Mr. Crosby, but let me ask Al, "Can you forget my name and my presumed religion while I work? If I'm competent to do the job, what difference does my name make? I expect to be judged on my competence, *not* on my name or what you think my faith may be!"

I was quiet through most of the dialogue and was thinking of playing "musical departments" with the engineers; yet, that seemed like a dead end since most of the visiting engineers in the group had Jewish names, Zimmerman, Goldman, Newman, and so on. But I was a bit relieved by the dialogue if the accommodations which Al and George were making worked out.

The meeting lasted but a few more minutes. Al shook hands with George and George shook hands with all of us, scooped up his sheaf of papers and headed for the tool crib. Al began to smile and talk with Jim in his Irish brogue apologizing for his bias and telling Jim about his interaction with local Jews.

I walked away with Jim and expressed my surprise by the anti-Semitism we'd seen. Jim smiled and said, "Of course! Isn't it the old matter of people justifying their behavior by mouthing that platitude claiming that 'some of my best friends are Jews?'"

As we walked toward Jim's office on the fifth floor, I shared the fact that I had trouble with anti-Semitism and anti-Franco feelings in my old Yankee family, especially with one uncle; but, despite (or because of?) my college education, I had been naïve about its thinking it didn't happen here. I thanked Jim for his skillful handling of the problem and my appreciation for an important learning experience.

5. IN TRANSITION

One morning shortly after seven I parked my bike in the rack near the Elm Street entrance of the Biddeford Division, intent to speak to the Personnel Manager and visit a couple of other people before going to the office to greet the engineering crew when they arrived at eight. Peering through Rusty Dennett's dirty office window, I saw that he was writing at his desk, but had no visitors.

"Hi, Rusty!"

"Oh, howdy, Roy. How's it goin' an' what can I do for ya?"

"I had a little extra time so decided to take a detour to the office this morning and to ask how you were making out finding us another clerk who either knows calculating machines or could learn quickly. By next week, our engineer guys will be getting ahead of the paper flow if we're not careful."

"Glad ya asked," Rusty said, jovial as usual. "This afternoon I'm interviewing a woman for the job; if she seems suitable, could I send her up between two and three? OK? Incidentally, Grace thinks you're doin' a great job coordinating this Cost Project."

"Thanks, Rusty, I'm doing my best. Incidentally, I've not seen you since Bill Watson died and we added Charlie Crogan to the crew . . . and I've got a great story to tell you about Charlie." So I regaled him with the story of Charlie and the New York Yankees "Incidentally," I added, "did you know that part of his work history?"

Rusty snickered as he responded. "No, I didn't! Evidently he thought it wise not to do so during our interview since he was here in Red Sox territory. If I had known and told ya, I'd certainly have ragged ya about becoming a traitor here in Red Sox Land! What a story! And how's he doin' learning the Frieden calculator?"

"He's coming along, if a bit slowly. I think he'll be OK when we need him most; we're just starting the major computations as Grace may have told you." As I turned to leave, I shot back, "Then I'll probably be hearing from you this afternoon? I'll warn Grace and Priscilla about it in case I am called away from my desk by Kettley, Black or emergency."

Rusty looked up, knowingly.

Stepping a few steps along to the packing room, filled with smells of tar from the huge bolts of a special tar-coated paper in which S-L-S shipped machinery and repair parts all over the world, I spied Tubby leaning over a desk seeming to hang precariously from the packing room walls. He was one of the shop foremen I had known longest. How he got away from his shops' responsibility at mid-day, I never knew, but he also had a job as umpire for Telegram League baseball games each spring; Thornton Academy was part of that League. He invariably showed up with his six-inch-thick inflated chest pad which along with his protruding belly cut quite a figure among high school athletes. Every time I saw him, I could imagine he was just bouncing another foul ball off his chest and getting snickers from the crowd! When he lined up behind a catcher, it was a wonder that anything got thru that solid defense. He tolerated no nonsense. A strike was a strike and a ball a ball. And if somebody slid home and he called them out, no coach could shout or shock him out of it! They knew better!

On that particular morning, I addressed him as "Mike." I

knew that he was generally known as "Tubby," but I didn't feel comfortable calling him by such a nickname. He looked up and smiled, remarked, "My gawd if it's not that old second-basemen with two left thumbs!"

I laughed a good laugh. In one close game with Biddeford, I made two errors in one play at my second-base position, one fielding and one throwing. Unfortunately, I came to bat first in our half of the inning. As I took a couple of practice swings before the pitcher threw the first ball, Mike remarked with a smile that I could see through his ump's mask "Roy, you got two left thumbs!" Whenever I saw him after that, in the shop, on the street or at another ball game, he always said, "Ah here's the guy with two left thumbs!" It was no different that morning, but we had a good laugh together. But I always felt that he really liked me and I could "take it" and so responded accordingly.

"How ya doin'?" he asked.

"Some progress," I asserted.

"Tough job, but I've begun to figure average sizes of boxes and the cost of each. Some day soon we'll sit down and go over the figures."

"Great!"

Leaving Mike, I strolled slowly across the room to find Dan Grady, just sitting down to his desk and grabbing a clip board full of Bills of Lading and other shipping documents.

I stepped into his office unceremoniously and addressed him, "How's Dan, the Singer?" I'd known him since I was a boy because he was a neighbor and dad had serviced his car, talked with him like the proverbial Dutch uncle; he came from a prominent local Irish family, had an army of brothers and sisters, was a big-wig layman in Saco's Most Holy Trinity Church, had a crisp and strong tenor voice. Sometimes he and dad would pretend to harmonize as he entered the garage. He had taught me the verses of a popular song that began, "Long ago, and far away," once sang it for me in his office while his office mates pretended to dislike it and held their hands over their ears! This morning, he simply held one note while I smiled.

"How goes the battle?" I enquired.

"Fine, Roy; I'm coordinating my analysis with Mike; as he may have told you, we'll have figures for you soon. I think that Kettley is smart to be looking ahead to save our asses when the goddamned war is over. I assume you think so, too, or you'd not be working the 25-hour day with those overpaid guys you're guiding around this sweat shop . . . .although I keep asking myself why our Cost Department buddies can't or won't do the job; after all we have a hundred years of records."

I did not rise to meet his criticism. I was simply glad he felt free to express what he felt about the Project. But, I did say, "They told 'RAK' [Kettley] that it would take five years and I'm trying to learn whether or not the Bedaux System has fouled up the process? Have no insights yet. But I'm suspicious of outside pressure from the government!"

"Wouldn't surprise me if that was a factor," Dan opined. "I'd rather see the money we're spending on that project distributed among foremen; that rule about getting no time and a half for hours over forty really gripes me."

I didn't comment on that; after all, I nearly went under with our personal finances because of that Shops-rule. But I did say, "Dan, I've looked at the question of outside pressure, too, and can hardly wait to talk with our Congressman about it. Meanwhile, I guess we must keep on keeping on with the process that is giving us lots of data about our textile machines and their spare parts."

"Right, Roy, good luck."

I thanked him and hastened toward the office.

29

6. A CROWDED SCHEDULE

When I reached the office, an hour later than usual, two of the engineers were waiting to see me, and Grace reported on three phone calls:

. . . Mark Black wanted to see me at 11 because we had an 11:15 meeting with Kettley;

. . . Rusty Dennett confirmed our two o'clock meeting with the prospect for another cost data processor;

. . . my father wanted me to phone tonight after seven.

"Anything wrong?" I queried.

"I don't think so," Grace said, "He said he wanted to make an appointment to see you."

"Hmmm, that's strange," I mused, "he knows where I am."

"I suggested that he come over, but he said he knew you were busy at the office and worked long hours and were tied up evenings. Did he leave a number for calling back?"

"Yes."

"Would you phone him and tell him that that I'll come over where he's working when I can get away? Meanwhile, let me see what Al Newman wants."

So I joined Al in the section where the engineers had their own private tables.

"Roy, I've run into a technical problem downstairs in heavy milling where Lou Butterfield holds the fort. He's working on the head end for a twisting machine being made for E. I. Dupont Company, but the machine that we've chosen to represent spinning varies somewhat from those twisters. What shall we do?"

Since I'd been there before, I suggested: "Look, Al, Lou Butterfield's one of those guys who knows compromise when he sees it; otherwise he'd not have been Mayor of Saco for a term or two. Use blueprints for both machines and have him show you the differences and how the assembly of each differs so you can get an exact costing for each machine. I don't think that the differences are so great that you can't figure out what we need."

"OK, Roy, but what do I need in the way of new blueprints?"

"Have Priscilla work it out and get you the extra prints that you need; also, before you feed your data into that mass of stuff that's coming up, flag it so we'll know here in the office what we have to do. Maybe you could have Priscilla make the parts lists on colored paper so we can't miss it. O.K.?"

"OK, and thanks," Al said before he dashed off to Heavy Milling.

I then sought Priscilla to alert her to what Al needed to do. I knew she was probably in the Reproduction Room so I strolled across the hall to find her. Sure enough, she was at the big blueprint machine, looked up and held up her fingers to indicate she'd be with me in two minutes. This gave me an opportunity to say a word to Herb Lavallee, a person I'd meant to visit since seeing him at the crucial meeting that Mark Black held for personnel in Specs, List and Reproduction, his three departments, a month before to give them an overview of the Cost Project and insisted upon their cooperation; Ralph Perry had clued me on the nature of that session since I'd had to leave early. But I didn't have many details.

So I said hello to Herb, really not knowing how he might

regard the project. He was quite cool to my "Hello," merely looked at me with some disdain as he echoed my "Hello" with one of his typically indifferent salutations, then turned away.

I had had my differences with him during my first year at S-L-S when he attempted to lure me into what was then a "gay" group that was shops-wide; yet those in the group had managed to maintain its interests and "business" in the "closet." He had arranged parties with some of the younger men and women in the three adjacent departments. Before I realized what was going on, he had given me books, neckties, etc and I was puzzled by what was happening. We had taken a camping trip together; but eventually I shed my innocence and dropped him cold; that didn't make him any too happy. But at work, he was usually quite correct, was efficient at his job. And that was all that I wanted. Fortunately, my sister absorbed any anger that might have exploded into action after my departure.

On that particular morning, he avowed that Priscilla was doing a good job in handling the extraordinary amount of work that the Cost Project was creating. I told him that I appreciated his cooperation and that we would certainly consider his own pressures while getting done what we needed to do. I stuck out my hand to confirm our informal arrangements, but he would not shake hands with me. He simply walked away to process the large blueprint he held in his hands. This did not surprise nor upset me. I wanted no trouble with him that might require Mark Black's reprimand or even stronger reaction. But I understood his anger. I knew that he feared that I might blow the formal cover to his homosexual group. Nor did I wish to encounter any physical violence and "wake up dead" under the gears or belts of some "wild machine" in the shops or catch part of "poorly handled ladle" of red hot metal in the foundry. I knew that that was always an imminent danger because it was part of the legendary stories about strange deaths that had occurred in that hot place, legendary and persistent through the years. It was always in my mind and peripheral vision when I walked through the foundry and saw the asbestos-clad workers pouring castings. In fact, it was one reason why I took the long and safer route around the foundry if my trip to or from the shops happened during the high (and hot) times that that procedure was at its max.

Back at my desk, I phoned my dad who was now working as an inspector on both the Ford bogey wheel and Sylvania fusecan (detonating weapons for anti-submarine warfare) jobs, filling in when some of the women were on their rest periods. He had finally concluded that running his own private garage was costing him more energy and uncollectible funds than his nervous system could "take," that he'd better build up some Social Security backlog, at age fifty. It was an enormously heavy decision at his age because he'd started his own business, liked being his own boss and had little financial security. To my surprise, he asked for my opinion about making a work shift shortly after the war began. He had a somewhat romantic approach when starting a garage, for it fulfilled a dream he'd had since viewing his first automobile "up country" near his boyhood home at Salmon Falls. But now he had a more realistic outlook after those years of experience, living on a shoestring while running a "back-street" garage at the northern edge of Saco and having to rely on my mother's income from serving as laundress for a few wealthy Saco families.

When he finally came to the phone, he simply asked, "Can we have a bag lunch together over here at the Ford or Sylvania job tomorrow noon? I can have your mother make a lunch for you." I thought for a moment, then said, "Of course," I'll meet you at noon."

Black and Kettley Check Progress

When I met Mark Black a little later before meeting with the CEO, he warned me, "Kettley knows about Calligan's confrontation with George Spielman and wants to learn whether or not you've encountered much of that attitude around the shops. Also, he's sensitive about the need to meet some short-term objectives. I think those are the two big issues.

That forewarning helped me keep my perspective, for I knew that Kettley was rumored to have a short fuse and had been known to fire people on the spot if they didn't live up to his expectations . . . .and those were not always clear.

Entering the office, Mark shook hands with the Kettley and turned quickly to speak to Lawrence Perry, who was standing by and who I knew as Kettley's secretary. Meanwhile, I shook hands with the CEO then turned to speak with Lawrence, Ralph's brother, whom I'd known almost as long as I'd worked at Saco-Lowell.

Kettley began and immediately announced, "I've asked Lawrence to sit in so he can help us monitor our progress; also, since I am responsible for coming up with overhead figures for each department, I'm going to put him on that detail. You know him, Roy, so that should facilitate communication.

"First I want to inform you that I know about Al Calligan's altercation with Spielman and the anti-Semitism you encountered. It had not occurred to me that this would happen even though I inferred from the list of our engineers that most of them were Jewish. Roy, did you have any inkling of any problem in this regard?"

"Mr. Kettley, the prospects of a problem raced through my mind when I first read the list of engineers joining us, but I had never heard of an incident here in the Shops so I assumed all would be OK. Similar to that issue, however, I had encountered some anti-Franco-American biases and thought that the pressure of the project might reveal some of those sticky points? But so far, that's been no problem even though some of the engineers, most of whom are pretty worldly wise and experienced, have asked me about this in the context of local mores. Another, a former football player and now an NFL fan, asked me about the Battle of the Bridge and Thornton-Biddeford High School conflict; and, though he doesn't know if he'll be here for the football season, he seemed a bit apprehensive about it. I assured him that he probably didn't have anything to worry about."

Kettley had been very attentive during my brief reaction to his question, then he asked, "If you encounter any more situations like this, would you talk with Lawrence about it; I'd rather handle it from the top down rather than having the Superintendents involved as Jim Crosby was at the Gear Job."

"I understand, sir."

"Finally, Mark and Roy: how are we progressing? Are these hot-shot engineers earning their keep? And will we be meeting our target to be ready to go to OPA in December or January? It's almost the end of July; how is the data flowing in? And have you finished any one machine of the nineteen we chose to study?"

I responded: "I think that we'll soon be able to collate the data on the Kitson line of machines, but we'll be needing some overhead percentages for some of the departments pretty soon. I'll review that need early next week, relaying the relevant department names to Lawrence where we'll soon need that info. As you know, parts for some machines are processed from every department in the shops."

"Yes, I understand that and I don't want to push you into a crisis mode. Your proposal and timing sound OK to me. In fact, it sounds as though you have the entire project under control."

"Thank you, sir, and thanks for your understanding. We're not quite to a 'full-court press.'"

Kettley smiled and the conference was over.

Walking back to Mark's office, Mark put his arm around my shoulder and congratulated me for handling the anti-Semitism incident smoothly. He went on to say, "In all my years at Saco-Lowell, I've never encountered such a situation."

I picked up the topic and observed, "That may be because we've not had such an 'intrusion' of 'outsiders' in this part of the textile industry; also, Saco and Biddeford are mostly Francos and old Yankee families. I have an uncle who is 100% anti-Semitic. He once told me in my parents' very kitchen that he thought Adolph Hitler had done a great job killing the 6,000,000 Jews. I argued heatedly and nearly had a fight with him, pointing out that he would probably be at the top of any list of Yankees who were victims of any purge of Yankees in New England; but, in deference to mother and dad, I cooled my tongue!"

"I assume that was E. A.?"

"Yes," I replied, but did not continue the discussion since we were nearly back to Mark's office door.

When I returned to my office, everybody was headed for lunch so I decided it was a good time to follow my pledge to myself: to take some quiet time for reading. While I knew I should be studying German for entrance exams to graduate school, I had also decided to read Thomas Mann's *The Magic Mountain* that summer. That may have been a poor choice, but I was a chapter or three along before taking it to the shops as "recreational reading." So I settled down at my desk. The two young women who had remained at the office instead of going up town to eat at a popular restaurant gave me the space I needed. The sun poured in the south-facing windows and I practically tasted the heaviness of Hans Catsorp's story of going to the tuberculosis sanitarium with dreams that gradually became transformed as he felt the aura and magnitude of the mountains. Pretty heavy reading, yet I was interested in the ironies and paradoxes that I encountered. And, indeed, it did carry me far from the world of textiles, costs and human connections. I wondered how my own world and that of my family might be similarly affected by these days at Saco-Lowell and my forthcoming work for a PhD at Harvard.

7. NEW & ROUTINE PROBLEMS

Speaking of earning and saving money for Harvard, Maryllyn and I rented a small attic apartment in Biddeford; and although it was unbearably hot, we decided to stay for the summer; it was in close proximity to both the hospital and Saco Lowell. I remember that the small room was conducive to important discussion; also I recall listening to an FDR radio speech that eventually became known as "My Little Dog Fala" speech. At that time, still being an unreconstructed Republican, I was not too impressed; yet we listened as we wiped the perspiration from our faces and discussed Maryllyn's work at the local hospital. Also I spent an hour many evenings "boning up" on my German since I had to take a language exam before starting courses at Harvard.

We also discussed some of the chores we needed to do before beginning that journey. There was always a money problem, and we reviewed how we would travel back and forth from our attic apartment to M's family cottage at Granite Point, considering the fact that we were always low on our gas rationing coupons. Donna, living with her grandparents, needed to see us. Also, we needed to continue our week-end clam-digging exploits not only digging a bushel or two of clams per tide but also selling them to add to the "kitty" we were building up for graduate school.

On the particular night following communicating with dad, I said to Maryllyn, "Dad wants to have lunch with me tomorrow, I wonder what he wants? Surely he knows that we have enough gasoline to get to his house in Saco."

"Maybe he wants to see you alone, dear?"

"Possibly; anyway, I'll find out tomorrow."

Next day after a reasonably calm morning, I meandered my way to the Erecting Room where both Ford and Sylvania assembly lines were in process. That's where dad worked. Since he was expecting me, he'd left the line and was waiting at the rest room where employees became somewhat insulated from the inevitably noisy machines around them.

Since I was a moment or two late, he had already started to eat. He handed me the bag lunch that mother had promised to send even as I said, "Hi! Dad!, Good to see you." We dealt in "catching-up" talk, mother's and his health, the Cost Project and Priscilla's part in it. Finally, I asked, "And how's your work coming along? Do you like what you're doing?"

"That's why I want to see you."

"Is there trouble?" I inquired.

"No, not really, but . . . "

"But what . . . ?" for I could see he was beginning to tear up as I'd observed before and the family attributing those situations to his "nervous breakdown "of fifteen years before. But I didn't press with more questions, and he gradually calmed down.

"I don't know if I can handle this job much longer. I like the inspection job on these Sylvania cans or fuse containers for submarine warfare and am holding my own on the assembly line. I don't know where these sharp-edged bastardly 'cans' come from, but they sure do come like hell! And they sure do cut up my hands (and he held them out for me to see) and I've chopped up three pairs of leather gloves testing them with the 'Go' and

'No Go' gauges. Both the guys and the gals working here call me 'Grampa' in a neighborly sorta way and occasionally help me if I get behind. But my hands hurt a lot of the time, and maybe I should ask to move to the Ford job where the castings are smoother? But, really, Roy, I think this will work out OK. I like the foreman, too."

Noting again that he was disturbed, I suggested, "Dad, let's walk to the other end of the building . . . which we did.

Then, strolling back thru a bank of thundering stamping machines, making washers out of sheet steel, dad continued. "You know, Roy, the other thing that's bothering me as much if not more than the sharp Sylvania can edges is the rest room. With no doors on the johns and the open sawdust boxes both guys and gals use as spittoons for their tobacco chewing, it's nasty and stinks! I know I'm old fashioned and all your life you've heard your mother and me rave and rant about bathing in cigarette smoke."

"WOW, dad, I've seen these intolerable conditions, but never thought how you might be caught, especially by the violation of privacy in the toilets. Can't the union stewards do anything about it?"

"Damn it, Roy, they're part of the problem!"

"Hey, dad, while growing up in your garage, I was told that I should change the problem if I couldn't solve it."

"Yeah, that's the story of my life, but how can do it here where we're all cogs in the wheels whether we're working on an inspection line or an automatic screw machine. And look at those poor guys and gals working on those stamping machines we just passed down the aisle!"

"Well, dad, I don't know if I can do anything about it, but I can try. I have the ear of top management so I can easily discuss the matter with them. Meanwhile, you could find another job or try to rig up a fan or work by a window or even 'talk turkey' with others who work with you. I suspect that when it's hot and humid in the summer, it doesn't matter."

"Some of my friends say that."

"OK, dad, I've gotta go back to the office. Maryllyn and I will try to get up to the house soon to see you and mother. Maybe we can bring Donna on Sunday?"

The one o'clock whistle blew and dad said, "Thanks for listening" and scuffed slowly back to the assembly line. Hiking quickly back to the Cost Project office, I dashed quickly into the rest areas of three shop departments and found them all with conditions similar to the one that dad used. Quickly, I said to myself, "Surely doors could be put on the rest rooms easily enough? And surely we have them in the office rest rooms, why not in the shops'? Wonder what Mark might think?"

Seeing him in his office as I neared my own, I popped my head through his door with the query, "Got a minute?"

"Yeah, just about one!"

I quickly told him the story about toilets; fortunately, he'd known dad for many years, used dad to repair his cars, knew our whole family pretty well. I saw him make notes on his ubiquitous note pad, then dashed away with the thought: "Maybe he can change the problem?"

Back at my desk, I asked Grace if she'd ever heard her husband, Rusty, speak of the rest room situation . . . though I did not tell her what precipitated the question.

She replied, "A couple of times, but he blamed the sanitary conditions on the union stewards who in turn blamed the situation on the quality of the janitors who blamed it on the nature of the physical buildings and plumbing and on and on . . . "

"And I suppose they blamed it on the seagulls that circle the plant?" I added sarcastically.

Grace laughed and said, "No doubt. But I've never heard any employee movement in the direction of doing something about it!"

I thanked her and called Priscilla from across the room. "How'd you make out getting Al Neuman's blueprints ready for discussion with Lou B. down in Heavy Milling?"

"OK," she replied. "He's had one meeting with Lou so all seems well."

"And how are you coming along yourself?"

"Fine, except for the fact that Herb LaVallee is pretty cold, sometimes makes some pretty sarcastic remarks about you! And I don't know what that's all about!"

"A long story, sister, and I'll tell you about it some day. But I have another question for you."

"What's that?"

"Have you seen the folks recently?"

"Yeah, Elwood was away bass fishing last week-end, so I took the boys up to see them. They seemed OK although dad was nursing his hands that he'd cut on the Sylvania cans. Otherwise, mom seemed OK, is feeling better about their income and outlook for retirement than when he was running the garage and couldn't collect from the deadbeats he did work for all those years. I thought you'd been there recently to see for yourself. Why do you ask?"

I briefly summarized my meeting and lunch with dad, then we were cut off by a phone call and didn't get back to the topic until later. But I did ask "Priscilla, would you check the women's rest rooms in this building and those in the Shop and report back as to whether or not they have doors on the individual stalls?"

"Doors on the stalls?" she exclaimed, quizzically.

"Yes, doors . . ." The phone rang again and she went off shaking her head, seemingly puzzled!

The call was from John MacScott, foreman of Saco Sheet Metals and Painting Departments and he was hopping mad when he ordered me, "Fairfield, get your ass over here and right *now*!"

I asked, "What's the matter, John?"

He swore at length, "Never mind, get over *now*!"

He'd spoken loudly enough that Grace, just back from lunch, heard the conversation, turned in her swivel chair, laughed and remarked, "He doesn't sound like a very happy camper!"

"Probably he lost his package of Tums at lunch," I replied, then added, "Wouldn't surprise me if Fritz Zimmerman were giving him fits!" as I headed for the Saco division of the shops I didn't break stride hustling across the river on the narrow steel and asbestos bridge; yet, I saw how low the river was and knew we were having a dry summer season. Since John MacScott's department was the first one in the building, I was soon striding down through the metal cutting and bending machines and entering his office. Sure enough, he and Zimmerman were staring silently at one another. I addressed them both, "Gentlemen!"

John snapped, "He's no gentleman. He's a Jew . . . !"

I cut him off, looked him straight in the eyes, "Look, John, you must have heard about the incident with Al Calligan on the Gear Job; also how we resolved it! Fritz has been here for several weeks and now you're complaining about his religion! Come off it! I have just one question: Is he doing his job?"

John's response: "I don't know, but his writing is so small and he's so slow; I want to get him out of here. He's constantly asking questions as he moves through your parts sheets."

I turned to Fritz and asked, "Is that your perception of what's happening?"

Fritz was soft spoken and quietly replied, "I'm trying to

43

understand how pieces of these opening machines fit together; I've spoken to my colleagues when I've gotten boxed into a corner. I thought we were being asked to do a thorough job and didn't know that I had one of Bedaux's time-study men on my back; John has not mentioned this until today when I came in to check my latest list of parts to be costed out."

I knew that MacScott had a reputation for being abusive because one of my dad's old friends, who worked in the Paint Department, had felt the heat of his tongue as well as his threats and short fuse. So I said to John. "Let's step out in the shop and walk down to the bridge and across the river, maybe that will help us cool off?"

John said nothing and we strolled past his noisy machines with their "Clump!–Clump-Clumping" sounds where in the past I had watched both men and women pushing their hands dangerously close to the blades that cut the steel panels. When beyond the reach of those ripping and shredding sounds and standing at an open window on the bridge, I said, "John, I'm aware that Zimmerman is a very meticulous man. Maybe he doesn't belong on this Cost Job, but he's here. If your concern is really his speed, that's one thing, but I have to agree with Jim Crosby that Fritz' religion is none of our damned business. He could be an atheist or communist and I could care less. So long as he has the usual Saco-Lowell work ethic, that's all I care about. And that's Crosby's and Kettley's point of view. As I flip through his parts sheets, he seems to be competent. In fact, John, he's probably overqualified for the job he's on. Has he told you about the machine he invented to plane propellers for ocean-going ships and they're even using them on the Liberty Ships in the South Portland Shipyard?"

"Yes, and he wanted me to look through the manual and blueprints for the planer, but I told him I was boo busy to do it."

44

"John, I can understand the pressure you bear every day supervising a herd of machinists and a half dozen painters, plus an assistant foreman, and all that that means. But none of you will have any job if we don't finish this Cost Project and get price relief from the OPA! You heard Jim Crosby on that topic."

"Yeah, I know, I know," John retorted. "Nor do I object to his religion. Guess I just flew off the handle."

"I hope it was only that, John; we surely don't want scuttle-butt from another Calligan-Spielman incident noising around the shops. None of us has anything to gain from it."

As we returned toward the office and saw Fritz bent over his blueprints and work sheets, I changed the subject to something less controversial, "John, since I'm over here, do you have a moment to talk with me and my old family friend, Woody DiPierre? We haven't yet designed cost sheets to include the painting process. Would you be willing to help me do that? I'm not quite sure how many steps there are when treating the surfaces of all these huge textile machines. And do they differ from cast iron parts that you have laid out in what looks like squadrons!"

"Squadrons, no, but army divisions, yes!" And he chuckled as he mouthed the word "squadron" silently. John had cooled off by now and we walked together to find Woody in his "space suit" spraying a gray paint onto a large panel that looked like the side of a carding machine. John concurred with my identification, then signaled Woody to come out of the paint booth and take off his mask. When Woody was unencumbered from his paint suit, I said "Hi," sniffed the air and thought I detected some kind of banana oil present and quickly noted, "If that's banana oil, Woody, we need to walk to an open window. I once got deathly sick when dad was painting a car, using some of that stuff."

"That's what it is," he remarked quite matter-of-factly. "My

45

lungs must be full of it, but we can't do much about it as John knows. And we've been over this problem a thousand times, with shop stewards and paint manufacturing reps."

John interjected, "Woody's right and we're still working on it. Would you take Roy from machine part to part and explain to him the various steps we take to prepare the various surfaces before and after assembly to prepare the metals. Unfortunately, we don't have a full spread of machines in process, but as you know we do have a few standard ones in process for the post-war orders. If you have to go up to Joe Kelly's Slasher Department to see more, go ahead. Woody, let Slim finish up what you've started. I've 'gotta' go back to the office to answer a question Fritz Zimmerman asked me right after lunch."

I shook hands with John, said, "Thanks for the understanding," smiled. He smiled back and walked away.

For the next two hours, I got the painting tour-treatment, first on the ground floor and then on the top deck of the Saco building where Joe Kelly and Woody took me through the various steps for the various Slasher parts; I got the same treatment in the card and drawing frame departments. Hence, in my mind I could design a form to accomplish our needs.

In the middle of that orientation, Grace called from the office to ask, "When do you need the information about the women's rest room doors? Priscilla has it ready except for the Saco building. I thought that since you were over there, you might figure a way to save time by having somebody else do it?"

"Grace, I can use it anytime. I'm going to see Mark next week sometime. No special hurry. I'd like Priscilla to do it when she gets slack between reproduction jobs. I think it best *not* to discuss it generally, as I told her and that it's best that one person do it. But thanks for calling. I should be back by four o'clock. Is everything else all right?"

"All's OK!" she reported.

Having cleared the air around Fritz Zimmerman and hoping I'd calmed John MacScott as well as collected information leading to costing painting processes for both Saco and Biddeford processes, I decided to stop a moment to see how my old friends and associates were making out accounting for excess tools in the Bendix tool crib as well as the Termination Department. Knowing my passion for four o'clock tea, Irene made a fresh pot and Harry, she and I gossiped a bit about progress in that space.

"Roy, we need your help," Harry Sawyer began. You'll recall that early in our tool identification era, we discovered that some of the heavy jigs and fixtures for the Ford job came in by way of Shipping, sent to the Ford assembly job and then on to Lou Butterfield's Heavy Milling Department . . . or at least we thought so. But Lou claims and his records support the fact that only five of the six ever reached his department; and, as you well know, Boston Ordinance will not reimburse us unless we find the castings even if we milled it for only ten seconds!"

"I understand your dilemma," I affirmed. I thought for a moment and then asked, "Have you systematically checked every step from the moment the print came off Harry Jones' drafting board, through the Purchasing Department, to the Casting Company, thru Wynn Frost's expediting process, to our Receiving Department, to our Transportation Division? Maybe it fell off one of our tractor trailers and slid into the Saco River?" I mused. Irene and Harry laughed!

I laughed, too, and said, "Stranger accidents than that have happened around here, sometimes deliberately!"

Harry interrupted me, "Stop! Stop! Stop! Wait! You're taking us off the track. Your imagination is getting the better of you!"

"Maybe," I smiled. "Did you ever hear the story of the

machinist who tried to sneak a medium-sized vise past Security, strapped it to his waste and hid it under a long loose raincoat? He stopped to speak to the guard at the Front Gate; the rope or belt that he used to strap it either broke or slipped and the vise fell directly in front of the guard. The 'thief,' looking down at his prize, remarked, 'Where in hell did that come from?' and walked on home. I never heard whether or not he was fired or forgot to come back, but it's a solid part of the mythology of industrial theft! In fact . . . "

"OK, Roy," Harry remarked. "We've all 'gotta' get back to work. Thanks for entertaining us. We'll follow up on the casting and we'll let you know how we make out!"

"Thanks for the tea and crumpets. See ya!"

They were still pouring castings when I detoured through the foundry, but I decided that talking with Wade Hansen would have to wait for another day. I was worn out and was still ninety minutes from punch-out time.

8. A MISCELLANY

Fritz Zimmerman had been the last of the engineers to check out the morning following my encounter with John MacScott; then, he was first to come in the following day. We had chatted briefly the night before and he had some reasonable doubts about John's honesty during our confrontation. No matter what John had said, Fritz believed that John's anti-Franco posture had slopped over into his attitude toward Jews.

"I've seen him walk up one side of his metal machine cutters and accuse them of doing things they hadn't done."

"For instance, Fritz?"

"The best illustration was his treatment of two Franco women who were working together on a metal trimming machine. Although they had positioned the guard and guide rails into position, 'cause I'd watched them put a heavy and awkwardly shaped part into place, he bawled them out for five full minutes in his Scottish brogue. It was something like watching a dog take a bone from an interloping animal. It was nasty, full of cursing and downright inhuman. I watched and listened but said nothing."

"Do you know if they complained to the Shop steward?" I asked . . . "because I can find out, Fritz"

"No, not now," Fritz warned, "that would make things even worse. John would know that I'd reported it. I'll soon be gone if you want to do it then. I don't want any more of his intimidation, I just wanted you to know how difficult it is to be honest with him. I think he's lorded it over his crew members so long as he's been foreman, he thinks that that's the way things get done."

"OK, Fritz, I'll let it go for the moment. How much longer do you think you'll need to finish up in that department, including the paint operations?"

"Probably a few more weeks," he estimated as he gathered up his papers and trudged heavily off to the Saco Division.

I was glad that my office colleagues had not been a party to that conversation, but I made some careful notes to which I might have to refer later, just as the phone rang. It was Lawrence Perry saying he had some of VP Kettley's data on overhead percentages. Could I come down to get them since he had to leave for a meeting soon?

So I walked to his office on the first floor, had a quick "Hello" and "So long" to Lawrence before returning via the Drafting Room where I stopped to see Harry Jones about the "lost fixture" for the Ford job. He had heard the story, but had not researched the matter himself, so I asked, "Harry, is there any defining feature of that fixture which might make it easier to find as they look under benches, in scrap piles, or anywhere? I think that Harry Sawyer and his assistant used a blueprint when looking for it, but they may have missed some subtle feature which you as designer might know better than they."

Harry looked up from under his drafting table light, pushed back on his high stool, stroked his chin and took another drag on his ever-present corncob pipe while contemplating. Finally he said, "Roy, there might be because it was to go on a lighter milling machine with a somewhat old and rickety carriage down in Lou Butterfield's joint. I'd say, if I remember correctly, that it might be a half inch thinner than its sister castings; also we had a special groove made into it so it would fit into that old carriage. He looked up as though his memory had been sparked, then quizzed me, "You know, I think that we made five regular and one special. Do you suppose that Lou's guys tried it, and it didn't fit so they sent it over to the assembly line thinking we would make a special adapter to handle it?"

"Good thought. I'll run down there this afternoon because I have to go see my old uncle who's just come back from an erecting job in Alabama."

"You can get an extra copy of the print from the tool print vault if you intend to look for yourself."

"Thanks, Harry. Will keep you posted."

Back at the "salt mine" after explaining to Priscilla what I needed for a print to search for the missing casting, I checked through the data on overhead percentages for most of the departments, including a few Kettley (RAK) had revised since his first report; I continued to wonder why he was so reluctant to include a percentage for the Foundry where most of the castings utilized in the shops were molded, then poured with red hot metal. But the list was at last here in time to begin figuring the cost of specific parts made on specific machines. Hence, with Priscilla and Grace almost caught up on their respective jobs, I sat down with them to get that lengthy operation started. In short, a particular part made on Drill Press X-23 might be graphed something like this:

Pt No.	Tex. Mach	Operation	Op'r'n.	Cost/min	O'vh'd	Tot
X-1	Picker	A	time for	$$$$	+% .	00

If at that time we'd had computer technology and spread sheets, these calculations would have been much less labor-intensive, so we had to do the best we could with what was available. Grace and Priscilla were very competent, Charlie, the ex-New York Yankee, was becoming proficient; Lennie, a former work-friend of Priscilla's, had come on the job, and her Saco-Lowell know-how about office lay-out and procedures made many of our everyday chores easier.

It was impossible to know exactly how many total operations there would be, but it was late July so we estimated we might have about a third of the shop work done. Once I'd started the calculations, I dropped a note to both Mark Black and R. A. Kettley, noting that we might have the shop work nearly done by the end of September or mid-October, hence that would leave a couple of months in which to complete the analysis and meet the early December deadline; but, I also reminded them of my impending departure on October 25. This last comment touched off a bell in Mark's head; for, before the end of the day he was on the phone reminding me, "We need to talk about your future. Let's try to meet next week." I said, "OK, if you have an opening next Monday, I'll come in." He responded, "Right after lunch?" "Fine," I said.

Since all of my "crew" were occupied and the fifteen engineers engaged in the shops, I decided to get in touch with Uncle Frank Benham who was doing a special erecting job on the Dupont twister job, one of the few domestic, presumably non-war orders in the shop's pipeline. Yet even these related to military work because we were building special machines for making extra-heavy tire cord for heavy-duty trucks transporting troops on the European front and were pointing toward the Japanese invasion somewhere "down the road." So to save an unnecessary trip into the shops, I phoned Don Brennan, who coordinated erectors' work in the Biddeford Plant; non-Biddeford erecting work was scheduled at corporate headquarters in

Boston. I recalled dad's saying that Uncle Frank was back, but would he be able to see me? Don didn't know at what stage of his work he was in, but suggested I phone him just before he was due to clock out around five. I did that and told him that I would like to see him for both personal and professional reasons. He sounded genial and receptive, suggested I come over to the Erecting Department first thing in the morning and if possible stay until noon because he was about to run tests with a variety of heart cams and gears to achieve the best tightening twist. So, I signed off, "Good to see you back!" . . . and he responded, "See ya' in the mornin'!"

Since I couldn't do much but review the engineers' work sheets, I did that. It also gave me an opportunity to touch base with "GL" [Spielman] who told Grace that he wanted to see me. I grimaced a bit when Grace told me, but remained watchful until time for us both to punch out.

He began, "Roy, I've been meaning to take you out to dinner and wonder if you could make it Friday? My wife's coming from home in New York and we'd like to have you and Maryllyn as guests at our hotel in Kennebunkport. Are you game?"

"I'll have to check with Maryllyn, but I think we're in the clear so long as we have somebody to take care of Donna."

"OK, right after work. We can swing by your place at Granite Point and take it from there."

After George left, I phoned Maryllyn, who said it would be OK although she was a bit apprehensive about having anything to contribute to the conversation.

I responded with, "Don't worry, dear, George Lincoln Spielman has been around the world and twice over; I'm not sure about his wife, but I'm sure we'll get a good dinner, one you'll not have to cook!"

Grace had heard the discussion. After he left, she asked,

53

"Have you heard anything about GL's date with Lennie?"

"What!" I exclaimed "Doesn't he know she's married?"

"I don't know," Grace retorted! "Lennie and her husband are breaking up so maybe she's looking for another man? She's young and pretty, so maybe he's a student of pretty faces? He's obviously a handsome man with many contacts. It could work. And after all, George is here by himself and maybe he's sowing wild oats?"

Grace and I looked at one another knowingly, and I said, "Perhaps best to keep this to ourselves."

"No doubt," Grace observed, then strolled slowly toward for time clock.

I mulled over the issues implicit in our various interchanges during the day, made notes for writing later in my journal, tried not to let the ethical issues distort my judgment about forthcoming conflicts.

9. UNCLE FRANK

I went to work early the next day, a Thursday, to check mail, interdepartmental memos, glance over each engineer's schedule for the day so I'd be sure to know where each was working. And when I got to the Erecting Floor, I first checked in with the Second Hand, Don Brennan, so he could flag me down if any vital phone calls came through. Grace and Priscilla knew where I was.

Looking through the row of posts that held up the third floor of the building and seeing Uncle Frank's bald head popping up and down beside the twister he was erecting, I went quietly to his side. Guess I was too quiet; as I walked up beside the machine on which he was working, he jumped as though I'd frightened him.

As I said, "Hi!" he smiled revealing his gold-inlaid front teeth and said, "Please respect my age and don't do that again. I knew you were coming, but didn't notice you were here."

As we shook hands, I told him that I was sorry and we picked up our conversation. "How does it seem to be back," I queried, "and how was Alabama?"

"Hot, too damned hot! The new Goodley Mills were installing air conditioning, but it was far from cooling anybody during the month I was there."

"So it's good to be back?" I asked. He said, "Sure, if you feel the need for A/C here, just open a window or door! That seemed to work when my friends at Saco & Biddeford Savings Bank requested A/C there a few years ago!" We both laughed as we sat on a couple of empty nail kegs beside the twister frame that looked something like the skeleton of a prehistoric animal.

"Before we get started on my lesson, Uncle Frank, I must ask you a personal question. Could you tell me more about Aunt Eva's death? Mom and dad have treated me like a child and wouldn't talk about it during all these years since she died, eight if I'm correct! What happened?"

He remained quiet for a moment, then began to tear up. I immediately cut in, touched his arm, said, "I didn't mean to upset you. As you well know, she was my favorite aunt; she talked with me incessantly all those years she slaved for the Lord Family while you were away putting textile mills together all over the world."

He resorted to his bandanna handkerchief, remained quiet for a moment, then began to pour out the words: "Roy, she was all I had in the world in the way of family except for your mother, father and you. We'd been married for twenty-four years. She couldn't have children though 'heaven only knows' that we tried. As you know, too, she served the Lord family faithfully as maid, cook, waitress, valet, chauffeur, seamstress, you name the chore and she did it. She even scheduled putting storm widows on and taking them off . . . and you'll recall how close we came to falling off those two damned ladders when putting on the windows that chilly October day ten years ago!"

"I thought we were both going to kill ourselves," I interjected as we exchanged nervous laughter.

"Well, to continue, she may have worked herself, literally, to death. I was not home on that fatal spring day when her appendix burst; she went to the Trull Hospital in a taxi (which she had called herself). Dr. Paul Hill, Sr. did the surgery and took out the remains of the appendix; but, upon close examination he saw that she was filled with cancer and never recovered enough to say 'Good-bye' to anybody. Harry Lord phoned me in Greensboro, South Carolina and asked me to come home as quickly as possible. I grabbed a night train to New York and gradually rumbled up the coast a day and a half later. I could hardly dare to look at her in the coffin; she was such a beautiful woman in so many ways. You were so close to her, and I watched you crying. At the time you told me that you didn't want to go to Quimby's Funeral Home and didn't like it that your mother and dad forced you to drive to Laurel Hill Cemetery in their car. When it was over, you showed me the scarf Eva had given you the previous Christmas and made you so proud. You promised me, 'I'll keep it always.'"

Uncle Frank stopped and leaned against the twister on which he was working.

Hot and uncomfortable as it was bathing in the mélange of noises and dusts filling the shop rooms, I was nearly in tears. Uncle Frank continued. "Roy, it wasn't over when it was over. My trip returning to my job in Greensboro was a dragging nightmare. In view of circumstances and the need to get those textile machines started, the Shops had agreed for me to go via sleeper, but that was filled with waiting on sidetracks to let express trains go through. There was a crash somewhere along the route. All I could see before my eyes was Eva's face, early and late; then I realized how much of our lives we'd spent apart; also, that she must have been in pain one day before I left on my last trip. We'd been out late dancing and she'd doubled up from pain in her right side. She sloughed it off, said it was 'nothing.' And I'll carry one thought to my grave, 'Why didn't I insist that she see Doc Hill immediately after that incident?' I should have insisted on it because she was in so much pain. I keep wondering how many of my fellow workers, making money and 'glory' for Saco-Lowell in all parts of the world, how many neglect their families the way I did?"

He again broke down and I suggested that maybe we should get together at some later time?

"*No*! Roy," he exclaimed, "I needed to get that off my chest! And you spent so many meaningful hours with her when I was away, that you deserve to know what happened. And now maybe I can renew our trips to Fenway Park as part of my payback time."

He paused and smiled. Then he asked, "Incidentally do you still have the baseball you found rolling down the front row behind home plate when we saw the Sox and Yankees play that summer? I think that was the same day you counted the visitor's catcher foul off eleven balls before hitting a home run!"

"Yep, I still have the ball, but I think that the marathon foul-ball hitting happened when I missed the only school day of my last seven years in grammar and high schools. That was when we went to see the New York Giants play the Braves at Braves Field in Boston. And it was Shanty Hogan who fouled off the eleven balls as the New York Giants won, eight to three!"

"OK, you've got a better memory than I. Nobody could forget the fun we had together. But now, Roy, what can I do to help you with the Cost Project. Don Brennan told me what you and those imported engineers are trying to do to save the company. How can I help?"

"Uncle Frank, I know basically that a twister looks something like a spinning frame, but for all my running about these Shops, I've never seen one in operation. And I was intrigued with something you said over the phone yesterday afternoon, that you were going to test some different sized gears or heart cams. Obviously, I had enough experience in dad's garage to know what cams are and what they do, but can you help me to understand that mechanism? Why are they so important for textile machines? Why does every machine need a half dozen of them as 'spare parts'?"

"Good questions, Roy, maybe I can and maybe I can't answer them, depending upon the specifications which E. I. Dupont has required for these machines. Unlike most spinning and twisters, which up to this point in textile history have processed wools and cotton, these are to be used for making strong cords by twisting together many strands of synthetic fiber. The fiber is synthetic and called 'Dacron,' something new under the sun!

"OK, back to basics: as you'll recall, cotton spinning requires three basic operations; namely, drafting or stretching the threads (made parallel when coming from previous steps or machines) which are elongated to reduce the diameter of the threads. In the second place, the threads are twisted together to make them stronger; and, thirdly, the threads are wound on the central core and made even stronger. Over the years these machines have become more sophisticated; at their best they'll perform all of the functions in one process or flow. The objective is to make them strong enough to work in the loom and withstand that motion as the warp is pulled in linear directions and the woof or filling moves up and down and through one another to weave cloth. That's an oversimplification, but I'm sure you get the picture, right?"

"Yes, that's a beautiful summary! Now, where do cams fit in?"

"Wait a minute, there's one other major factor we have to keep in mind. The fiber goes through rolls to do some of the twist and drawing, then is wound up on spindles designed to accomplish the three objectives. Hence the spindles travel at high speeds and the thread goes through rings which are spun by the spindles in a kind of drag motion. In other words, Roy, there's lots of motion created by a complicated relationships of gears, rolls, spindles and CAMS all coordinated to twist the threads, hence the name of the machine, 'twister.'"

"It's enough to make my head spin; always has been, every time I try to learn something about it," I said.

Uncle Frank chuckled, chewed the butt of a cigar, one of his trademarks, wiped sweat from his forehead.

"OK, to simplify, lets go sit in front of the head end since that's where the action or motion is controlled by gears and cams. I'll try not to be too technical, but let's follow the steps via blueprint, too; then, you'll have something to carry away with you if you wish."

"Good!"

Pointing alternately toward blueprint and machine, he called my attention to a train of gears which turned the so-called top rolls the full length of the frame. He then pointed to the gears that turned the spindles. Then he focused on what he called "traverse motion" which determined how far the thread would move back and forth on the rolls. Finally, he pointed out that there was a mechanism that lifted the thread up and down in order to wind the thread on the spindles.

"So far, so good?" he asked.

"OK, I follow you."

"Now," he began, "there has to be a subtle change of motion from moment to moment (or a coordination if you wish) so that the threads will attain their transformation in a uniformly wound way and be wound up and down the spindles evenly creating what is sometimes called 'a package,' a package that will be uniformly created so that it can be put into the loom to satisfy the strengths of warp and woof threads for that machine.

Well, the cams are necessary to change directions and speeds of all the motions. OK?"

"I think I get the general idea, Uncle Frank."

"Now, my job today is to try gears and cams as specified in paper specifications to see if all the theoretical prospects turn out to be accurate when the wheels begin to turn. By starting up the machine, even with a limited amount of thread on a limited number of spindles, we'll be testing the accuracy of the predictions. And if we need to substitute some of the gears and cams during the test, which might take one day or several, we'll know what to include when the contracted amounts are packed for shipment to the Dupont factory. I've oversimplified the technicalities, not to question your intelligence, but I may be here for more days than I like to think simply getting it right. Are you clear?"

I dodged the question but grunted something, like "clear as mud!"

"Oh, one other thing. The process contains a few variables because we don't quite know, either theoretically or practically, the narrow differences between the behavior of cotton and synthetics!"

"I think I get the overall picture better than in other times when reading or talking about it. But, I do have another question before I head back to my office."

"Go ahead, shoot!"

"What if there are some minor changes and they're built into the shipment for the entire lot of frames, what happens at the factory if you find other minor variations?"

"Roy, I'm surprised, have you *never* heard of 'the Biddeford fit'?"

"No. What's that?"

Uncle Frank chewed a bit more on his cigar stub, which had

remained unlit through most of our conversation, chuckled a bit, then proceeded.

"Except for the spindle assemblies where the tolerances are less than half a thousandth of an inch, these are low-tolerance machines. The average tolerance is probably five or ten thousandths of an inch. Good lord! I have even found them twenty. So, what do we do if things don't fit? We file the parts down with a good old-fashioned file until they don't vibrate or do something worse. Well, that filing is so common, we erectors call it making 'the Biddeford fit'!"

He then removed his cigar stub, resorted to his bandanna, spit in it, then leaned back on his nail-keg perch and let out a loud guffaw!

Although I wasn't too sure what to say, I joined his laughter. But I went on to ask, "OK, looking at this from a cost analysis viewpoint, what I'm currently doing, how can we establish an accurate cost value of your erecting and refining activity as well as all your prospective filing at the textile mill?"

"Good question, Roy, but you'll probably have to ask Kettley about it. I assume that each machine has it's own overhead at the Erecting Floor, also set-up charges when we go off to the mill to set up an order of machinery, no matter what or how many machines are involved. There are other unpredictable costs at the factory. I've been slowed down by strikes (both here and during the erecting process). Also I've been held up by having insufficient parts on location when somebody here neglected to pack the correct number or had to erect machine with incompetent help. Once, long ago at a new mill site, our machinery got lost in the bottom of a river, was eventually found, was badly rusted. In fact, that's why we now line the shipping boxes with a tarred, reinforced paper to preclude damage in transit. How on earth, Roy, are you going to build all of these contingencies or variables into the cost of any given part or any order for new ones?"

"By a system of overhead," I assume.

"Exactly! And Kettley is going to have to run that past you. None of us is a magician nor have a crystal ball for machine manufacturers!"

"True, true! OK, Uncle Frank. I appreciate your time and wisdom. Next time we meet, maybe we can talk baseball in more depth. Keep your eyes on the Red Sox, and thank a million."

I stood up, shook hands with him and dashed away toward the office, images of cams, gears and spindles whirling in my head.

10. OF LATHES, COGS & AUTOMATIC
SCREW MACHINES

Engine lathes were fairly common at Saco-Lowell. Although I never saw an inventory of them . . . after all, they were the traditional machine used to turn down any material "turn-downable," such as wood, steel, cast iron, bronze, brass, etc. And turning the axis of work from horizontal to vertical could recapitulate the ancient turntables used to create pottery. At S-L-S one or more types of lathe seemed available in almost every department, whether involved with shaping metal or wood. In his book, *Technics and Civilization*, Lewis Mumford argues that the use of an accurate lathe with a bar for resting cutting tools was the basis of the industrial revolution. Then building on the improved precision of that process over the years, Eli Whitney introduced the concept of interchangeable parts which further expanded that revolution!

One Saco-Lowell lathe became almost legendary. It seems that one employee in the five-story Biddeford Building decided that he could personally use a mini-engine lathe that graced his department. He took some rope, made a kind of sling to go around the little lathe, enlisted help to boost it up and out of a third-story window and began lowering it to a friend with a truck parked in the shops' yard beneath that window. From a distance a security guard saw it hanging just above the second-story window and ran to the truck. Having seen the guard coming, the compatriot on the ground signaled his companion overhead, then "got lost" midst nearby cars. The guard then decided to run up to the third floor from which rope, lathe and intent to steal derived. By the time he reached the window from which the rope and lathe hung, the second thief had disappeared! Then began a tug of war, with those on either end of the rope jigging the lathe back and forth, up and down . . . until the guard finally caught the receiver. But the would-be thief would not talk about his compatriot, simply said he didn't know anything about it. Although to my knowledge the men, especially the one on the ground, were never identified publicly, the originator of the plot was never caught. And the lathe became a ghost with a serial number, but was never found!

But that phantom lathe, like a vise that allegedly fell from another employee's waist as he passed the guardhouse, became part of the mythology and reality of industrial theft, along with the widely practiced "borrowing" of stationery, scrap paper, pencils, pens . . . and even typewriters from the office. I must confess that, short of paper at home, I occasionally borrowed scrap paper. In fact, I was recently looking through an old file, and found that I'd used abandoned lists of parts for copy paper in typing a few letters between 1936 and 1944! Then, too, it was fairly common at every industrial plant to experience theft of rare metals such as copper, aluminum and brass. At the Kittery Navy Yard, for instance, employees stole tons, literally, of those metals by hiding them in the channels of automobile frames and drove through the gates with impunity . . . until one employee was caught one afternoon when the guards employed mirrors to examine the underside of the cars when stopped at the exit gates for inspection and before being allowed to proceed toward home or some other destination . . . maybe a junk yard? My uncle, a chip-and-cocker of rivets on the submarines, witnessed the thieving process first-hand. There are probably records of the volume of such theft at the Yard; I know not who if anybody might have kept such records in Saco and Biddeford.

Well, I was somewhat acquainted with engine lathes. I had learned the principles and procedures of using them while attending Manual Training classes in the seventh-to-ninth grades at C. K. Burns School in Saco. Also, dad had a variety of lathes in his garage beside our Hutchins Street home. But I never acquired skills beyond the practice stage to make something of a serious nature at either school or home.

It was not difficult to design apt process sheets for our Cost Project. In fact, it was rather easy to teach Grace and Priscilla and their helpers to read the engineer-driven process sheets when the data came in from the shops to be analyzed and data compiled. Since each operation for each part supposedly carried a serial number of the machine on which a part was made, data used for compilation of the costing involved, the work could be done accurately and quickly. Only when it was not clear whether a part was made by a remodeled engine lathe or its newer "brother," the automatic screw machine, did we run into problems originating in one of the departments. Repeatedly, we cautioned our engineers to be especially careful to list serial numbers of the machines involved for each part. Then, by compiling a list of those machines for each department it was fairly routine to ascribe a value to each operation and part. When the engineers failed to indicate the serial number or reported that those numbers had been lost or chipped off the machine tools over the years, we had to meet with the shop foreman or second hand to clarify the numbers to indicate the type of machine related to any given part. On the particular Friday following my meeting with Uncle Frank, I decided to visit the department where most of the automatic screw machines ground out pieces at a phenomenal rate; it was high on the fifth floor in the Biddeford Plant, and I went over to talk with both our mechanical engineer and the supervisors of that department.

While I knew the basic operational procedures, it enhanced the process by asking the operator of a machine to compare the prints and the worksheets with the actual operation of the automatic screw machine. The foreman and second hand joined us beside the monster machines which consumed steel bars like hot cakes, making steel rolls for spinning machines, drilling holes, routing key grooves or cutting off washers, sleeves or other parts for the textile machines. Their explanations of the processes went smoothly and were virtually void of vibrations! The question arose: Why not utilize such machines for making more parts?

I asked both the foremen and tool designers that question. They had various answers pointing out that there were only a limited number of motions possible from any given point that a tool might reach. On the other hand a couple of our special cost engineers indicated that such expansive use was "happening" in new plants. One foreman suggested that I visit the Bendix job-site where anti-aircraft gun controls were being made and note that some of those machines, working mostly with aluminum and alloys, were at the edges of automation (which could eventually be computerized). Those terms and processes were not widely used in the United States until many years later.

But we had little difficulty solving our immediate uncertainties when "translating" our questions into cost analysis terms.

Some eighteen to twenty years later I had an amusing experience involving the term, "automatic screw machines." In an Ohio University classroom, I was attempting to explain how such a machine worked by chalking a crude diagram, in cross-section, on the blackboard showing how such a machine could be loaded with a variety of tools, such as drills, chamfers, chisels, etc. to perform multiple tasks without much labor after the set-up costs were figured in, hence was *not* labor-intensive. If I remember correctly, we were discussing various labor movements, especially the Luddites, wherein workers opposed and even smashed machines that would put them out of jobs. And surely, moving a productive process from an engine lathe where only one operation per set of tools could be effected, moving that process from engine lathe to automatic machine process did save time and money for the manufacturer!

Well, I did the demonstration on the black board, perhaps several times over a few years; then one evening a decade or so later while I was still based in Ohio, I received a phone call from Cleveland out of the "proverbial blue." The woman on the other end of the line, cautiously assured that I was "Roy Fairfield," then asked, "Do you remember one of your students who sat in the front row of that big social science class and always wore a canary yellow jumper?" I did, indeed, because she was ever alert as to what was happening in that class, also I remembered commending her for her work and how good it was to have her and her yellow jumper in the front row to alleviate the dullness of gray clothing and attitudes.

When I assured her that she was talking with the right person and it was good to hear from her although I confessed I probably would not have remembered her name if she hadn't given it to me, she went into a lengthy explanation as to why she called from Cleveland area to talk with me. She continued, "You know my classmates and I always thought that you were kidding us in your usual style when you talked about 'automatic screw machines' *until* tonight when I was reading *The Plain*

Dealer and saw an advertisement trying to employ an automatic screw machine operator."

For a moment I didn't "get it;" but, when I did, I broke into laughter so loud that I caught Maryllyn's attention elsewhere in the house! My former student laughed heartily, too. I then went on to ask about her life, what she was doing. And she asked about my life, too, the kind of discussion that teachers cherish because they learn that they've been heard or have made "the proverbial difference," however minor it might be. It was a memorable call! One might use a current cliché to say, "She made my day!" I suppose if I'd not spent so much time in those large lecture-hall classes attempting to reach the sixty to one hundred students' attention and involvement, that call might never have come in!

Interlude—Missy Laney Us

Returning to my office Saco-Lowell office via the foundry, I was dumb-founded to see my sister Priscilla weaving her way through the moulds in the foundry! My first reaction was to ask, "What in Sam Hill are you doing here?"

She laughed and said, "I haven't heard that fond expression of dad's since I got married and left home. What am I doing here? You asked me to check the women's rest rooms and I'm finishing the job here in the foundry; I completed the survey in Saco a few moments ago. It's a mixed bag, but I should have a typed summary by noon. Have you seen Mark since you asked me to do this survey?"

"No! But I had no idea you'd come into this hell hole to do the survey; it's a dangerous place to be at any time, but glad you're here in the morning and not afternoon when they're pouring red hot liquid into those moulds!" And I swept my arm across the brown moulds as though they were in a field.

"I understand your concern, Roy, but it might be more fun to watch than the piles of sand and lifeless moulds which I see right now!"

"OK, OK, I'll get off my hobby horse. Just be careful; see you back at the office!"

"OK, see you 'they-ah,'" and she stressed the Maine accent!

I kept moving too and looked back over my shoulder to be sure that she was being careful.

Back at the office, I wished Grace a good morning . . . or is it "Good noontime," I joked. "Guess who? I just met Priscilla in the foundry."

"Yeah, she said you probably would not like it that she was taking that route to do the digging about doors on the women's rest room stalls."

"What's a fella gonna do if his sister has no common sense?"

"But isn't a healthy curiosity a good human asset?"

"I thought we saved that for cats," I opined.

"Not if it increases the possibility of a *cat*-astrophe?" she punned, with stress on the "cat."

I laughed and responded with a "Brava! Now maybe I have a punning partner!" Grace turned back to her desk with the groan that one usually encounters with a pun. I continued, "Long ago, I concluded that nobody can lose with a pun. The pun-maker has fun and the groaner has fun. It's win-win and nobody can lose!"

"Never thought of it that way," Grace shot back over her shoulder.

I concluded: "Priscilla says she'll have a typed report for me later today; then I'll run it past Mark Black."

At that that moment the phone rang. Grace answered. "Harry Sawyer, wants to talk with you."

I picked up the phone. "Hi Harry, how's it going?"

70

"Good news," he began. "We found the missing casting from the Ford job. It's a slimy mess, but it checks out with the blueprint hence; it will be the crucial evidence when we encounter Army ordinance."

"Where'd you find it?"

"Down by the scrap iron pile beside the river!"

"Any notion of how it got there?"

"Well, some of the yard crew were laying pipe on that banking near the river, came upon an obstruction and that was it!"

"Do you think it accidentally fell in or did it have human hands to help? After all, the authorities once found Liberty Ship propeller shafts buried in a Brooklyn Shipyard, buried by machinists to assure their quotas when they fell behind production goals on a bad day!"

"I don't know, but we called the shop police and they're investigating it before we can bring it back to Termination; I hope it's an accident, but shop managers who've caught other thieves are saying it looks a little fishy. Gotten undetected out of the shops, it might have brought a pretty good figure in this day of high metal prices. And it was just rough enough to fool anybody unfamiliar with shop jigs and fixtures. There were only a couple of places where milling was required, and that matched nicely with the tool print. Harry Jones verified that."

"Anything you want me to do, Harry?"

"Not necessarily, Roy, but when the Army Ordinance lieutenants show up, you know them, so it might be helpful if you met with us so we'll be consistent in our procedures. The shop police may have the case solved by then. O. K.?"

"O.K., I'll be glad to help, and thanks for keeping me informed."

Hanging up, I relayed the information to Grace. She had a good memory and was superb in handling such matters.

A Serious Interchange

I worked on several minor issues and was about to eat my bag lunch along with more reading in Mann's *The Magic Mountain* when Joe Ainsley, our engineer working on the top roll job, strolled to the chair beside my desk and asked, "May I see you during the lunch hour? I have both a professional and a personal problem to discuss with you. And could we find a quiet place where I can talk freely?"

I said, "Since we both have bag lunches, would you mind if we talked and ate at the same time?"

"Not at all, but you may not be able to stomach the topic?" he said, in a quizzical mode.

"Guess we can start anyway if that's all right with you," I responded.

I'd had little interaction with Joe, but I was quite certain he and his engineer colleagues had dissected me from every possible angle. I'd overheard some of their discussions following the Al Calligan and John MacScott "Jewish Incidents." I didn't have many details to rely upon, but I felt confident that the engineers were mostly positive about me as the point man in this Cost Project. Well, adjoining our office, but with few doors and only a couple of windows, the Shop Research Department had a machine demonstration area with a couple of full-scale 1890 spinning and roving machines. It made a fine area for Drafting, Tool Design and Research employees to analyze machines on which they were trying new designs that were revolutionizing the textile machine industry. It was off-limits for most purposes, but I'd been given a key to the room to be used for conferences at my discretion.

I started with a bite of my sandwich and a query, "Well, Joe, I think we can speak frankly here, what can I do for you?"

Joe said, "Let's do the professional issue first. It's really quite simple. Mannie Boudreau, Foreman of the Top Rolls Department, seems a bit miffed because you've not visited him since we began this Cost Project; yet he's talked with other foremen in the shops who have told him you've visited them to check on how things were progressing."

"Did he tell you this or is this scuttlebutt?" I asked directly.

"He hinted this to me by asking how you were because he'd not seen you, except at the Superintendent's meeting in late May or early June. But scuttlebutt has it that you may be anti-Franco. As you know, he's one of the few foremen with a French-Canadian background and you're clearly from an old Yankee family. Something about your ancestors being wealthy land owners, governors, diplomats and prominent politicians . . . or something!"

I took a deep breath and a sip of tea from my thermos. Then, I became somewhat defensive and got right to the point: "Mannie's right that I've not visited him; also the scuttlebutt is correct that some of my ancestors were prominent Maine men. But believe me, Joe, none of that wealth nor residual power implications of it have ever filtered down to me! As proof, I had to scratch mightily to work my way through college and am now saving money to pay for graduate school. I don't think that I'm anti-Franco any more than I'm anti-Semitic. My immediate family was so anti-Franco and anti-Jewish that they drove me to believe just the opposite. Yet I suppose it was easy to pigeonhole me just as many people here in the shops stereotype others if they don't know them well."

I continued to munch on my lunch then asked, "What do you recommend beyond the obvious?"

Joe responded, "I'm no human-relations expert, but it probably would do no harm if you were to come over to the department and be seen with Mannie, his Second Hand and me. Also, I think you could profitably mix among the machinists there. I know you are interested in every damn operation of the machines we're costing out. In short, pay attention to them as responsible people."

"Good suggestion, Joe; I can do it right away, early next week."

"Terrific, but I recommend that you *not* say I suggested it."

"Do your engineering colleagues know you were going to try to talk with me about this?"

"No! I'm not too close with any of them."

"Fine, I simply don't want to cause a pandemic!"

"No worry," then he took another bite from his sandwich.

"OK, now to the personal question, Joe?"

"Roy, it's pretty raunchy, but you seem to have an open mind and I trust you'll understand."

"I'll try," I encouraged.

"Well, I went back home last weekend, to New York City. My wife greeted me coolly since I'd been gone 'a whole six weeks' and had phoned only once a week. I tried to explain this program to her, but she would have none of it, nor my arguing that we needed my income to keep up with payments on our Manhattan apartment, everyday expenses, etc. She kept saying, 'No way! No way!' I couldn't get her past that mantra.

"Finally I began asking her what she'd been doing because I'd had only one letter and two phone calls from her in six weeks. In the middle of that shouting match, the phone rang and we both made a dive for it. I won the race. It was a man who began, 'Hi, dear!' I handed her the phone and said, 'It's somebody saying 'Hi dear.' My wife grabbed the phone and started for the bedroom garbling her words to take me off course. I blocked the way to the bedroom; she continued to mumble over the phone and to cry. She finally hung up and turned to face my questions, 'Who was that and what was it all about?' An hour of querying revealed that she had a boyfriend and was planning to file for a divorce. Nothing that I could say dissuaded her. Finally, in desperation I picked up my suitcase, grabbed a cab for La Guardia and took the next plane back to Portland; in a rage I drove back to the Thatcher Hotel. Like a fool I began drinking scotch and was out of commission most of a couple days as you probably will know when you check out my time sheets.

"But I made a serious mistake. Last night I went to Saco's red light district, rented a 'virgin' or a least she was supposed to be one . . . "

I broke in . . . "Joe, are you sure you want to be telling me all this?"

Joe looked up a bit chagrined, stole a peek out the sun-drenched but dusty mill window and responded. "Yes, Roy, because it may affect our Cost Project . . . "

"O.K., if that's the case, although I don't see why . . . yet!"

"It gets worse and muddier." I was so angry with my wife, I wanted revenge so went into an 'I'll show her mode!'"

"In short," I interjected, "Destroy yourself to get even with her?"

"Yeah, something like that, but let me go on. I swear I'd never been in a whorehouse before, but was assured by the fact that the madam (or the woman running the place) claimed the girl was a virgin. I figured that that might save me from a vene-real disease. But when I got into this dimly-lit room and saw the young woman lying there, I suddenly wanted to retreat. When I spoke to her where she lay, half naked and half covered with a thin sheet, she moaned something that I couldn't understand. So I asked, 'What is it?'

"Again her response was more moan than words. I walked across the room and asked, 'May I put on the light?'

"She responded. 'Please don't.'

"Getting closer to her, I could smell blood and sweat. I sat gently on the bed, reached out my hand as if to touch her and she screamed, 'Don't touch me!'

"I should have left right then and there, but I didn't! Being in a strange place and on an uncomfortable mission, my first of the kind. My heart raced, but I sat quietly, could hear other understandable groanings and moanings in the house. That was not helped by an approaching thunder shower. You probably heard it yourself?"

"Yes, I did."

"Finally as her nerve and muscle spasms, a kind of shivering motion, ceased to vibrate the bed, I quietly said, 'I won't touch you, but please tell me what's the matter?' She cried a little then was quiet for what seemed an eternity. Finally she said: 'I was just brutalized by the man who was here before you, some guy who called himself "Pete" who's here from New York working at Saco-Lowell. I told him I was a virgin and wanted to be treated gently. He swore at me, pulled my legs apart and entered me like a steam engine. He screwed me for what seemed like forever. I thought he'd never stop.' She cried out in gasps, then continued, 'He ripped me so hard I may never stop bleeding. When I came in here, the boss of this place had told me to push the button on this cord if I needed help and she'd come to my side. I grabbed the cord and tried to push the button, but this guy who called himself 'Pete' ripped it out of my hands pounded on me time after time and time again.' All of this came in gasp after gasp!"

Joe was so agitated by telling the story that he suddenly paused to catch his breath.

I, too, took a long breath, then broke in with, "I don't know where this is going, Joe, but it sure 'ain't pretty.'"

"Nor do I know either, but I think we both know 'Pete,'" he said, knowingly.

76

"Did the girl ever regain her composure?"

"I offered to walk her to the office, but she said 'No.' I asked her if she had a family in Saco or Biddeford?"

"She said, 'No, I'm from Aroostook County, came here because there was no work in Northern Maine.' She went on to say, 'I'd better handle what may be a crime my own way. I can hitchhike back home, though I hate to think of facing my mother.' She began crying and sobbed, 'Leave, leave, leave . . . but thank you, thank you.' More sobbing, then she screamed 'I think I'll report this place to the police. You'd better go, go, *go*!' and she screamed so loud that the woman who had let me in came to the door, knocked and hollered, 'What's happening?'

"I was anxious to get out of there when I could, so I pushed the door, eased the woman aside, and got out of there as fast as I could!"

By this time my mind was somewhat jumbled and I asked, "What are you now afraid of?"

Joe looked somewhat sheepish and replied, "That I'm implicated if she does go to the police even though I never touched her!"

"Did you sign in when the so-called Madame took your money?"

"I'm so confused, I don't really remember?"

"Did the guy who preceded you leave his full name?"

"Again, I don't know. I don't even know if the house was registered with the police. Would you know?" Joe asked plaintively.

"How would I know?"

"But what does the law say?"

"Again I don't know!"

At that moment I saw Grace through the window of the office door and beckoned for her to come in. She partly opened it and asked, "Roy, the company operator wants to know if we have anybody here in our program whose name is 'Pete'?"

"Who's calling?" I asked, glancing at Joe.

"Somebody from the Saco Police Department."

I thought for a second, replied, "Not that I know of!"

"Thanks," and she closed the door.

Joe spoke up, "Now you know why I thought it important to tell you the story."

"But, Joe, I've never heard Herman called, 'Pete,' have you?"

"Yes, a couple of times, seems that that's his middle name; and he seems to fit the girl's description."

"So what do you think you should do now?"

"Since last night, when I didn't sleep much but drank too much, I've run this possible scenario thru my head a dozen ways and don't know what to say."

"And you didn't leave your name at the house?"

"I don't truly remember, things happened so fast!"

I remained silent, looked out the sun-drenched window and ran Joe's story through my head various ways. What if Pete did leave his proper first name? What if the girl reported the incident and didn't go into a local doctor or health facility . . . although I knew of no place except a hospital? What if she returned to Aroostook County and said nothing beyond report-ing it to the Saco police? What if the police came to interrogate me and my connection to these New York- based engineers? Now that I was pretty sure of Pete's identity, but might not admit it, could I be interrogated as well as implicated? Ques-tions . . . questions . . . if . . . if . . . if! Now, Joe's dilemma might become partly mine!

I turned to Joe and ran these various scenarios past him, and he expressed chagrin for his involvement. I assured him,

"Joe, I'm making no moral judgment of your visiting a house of prostitution, whether the place has a license or not. You certainly were in a frame of mind and inebriated condition to seek revenge upon your wife."

We discussed our respective dilemmas, but concluded our conference with the decision to discuss it with nobody. Maybe the incident would just go away? Surely, he should not at this time discuss it with Pete or any of his fellow engineers . . . and certainly not his wife. In other words *mum* should be the word. We then strolled out of the room; he went back to the roll job, and I assured him that I would soon visit his department and talk with his foreman. In a solemn mood, I said, "Maybe the problem will go away over next week end?"

Back in my office, I asked Grace to set up an appointment with Mannie Boudreau at the Roll Job, preferably for early the next week. Also, I said, "If the police or any other government official or representative calls, simply ask their name and number and tell them that I'll call them back as soon as possible." She assented and turned to her typewriter. In about half hour she handed me Priscilla's report on the shop's john stalls with open-versus-closed doors. I was glad she'd not forgotten.

I removed Mann's *The Magic Mountain* from my desktop to a draw, leaned back in my chair with bright afternoon sunlight pouring thru the dusty windows and scanned Priscilla's report. A half hour later, I suggested that she and I get together first thing Monday morning in the so-called "Conference Room" to discuss the report and how we would handle it. I also told her that we were going to pick up Donna on Sunday and visit our folk.

"Good," she noted, "because you know what? They've been asking about you!"

"Thanks for the tip. I need more pressure like the proverbial hole in the . . ." She may not have heard me because she bounced away with her usual flair.

I also remembered that Maryllyn and I were to have dinner with George Lincoln Spielman at the Colony Restaurant in Kennebunkport so I prepared to "close shop" myself.

11. SOCIAL INTERLUDE

George Lincoln ("GL") Spielman and his wife, Emma, were right on time to pick us up at Curtis Cove. George had dropped by once before to do paper work related to asking my other sister, Nancy, at Saco & Biddeford Mutual Savings, if she would help him with a banking problem, so he knew where we lived. We did the appropriate formalities and introductions, then headed for Kennebunkport in his Cadillac. On the way, we related to them the story of the ghost at Clock Farm, took a quick turn around Cape Porpoise Harbor to view the old colonial houses and further discuss Kennebunkport history. He had read a couple of Kenneth Roberts' historical novels so we had a lively conversation as we drove past the entrance to the well-known writer's estate.

At dinner George went into some depth about his boyhood in Germany, the Nazi treatment of Jews before the Holocaust, the early disappearance of his two grandparents. Much of this part of Nazi history was new to us at the time.

Emma was quite formal in her interaction, but she'd gone to nursing school so she and Maryllyn had much in common and shared some of their stories and experiences.

George went into considerable detail in discussing his brother's part in compiling a book on *World Ethics* which compared the common elements of the world's great religions, especially the ethical similarities and "commandments." But toward the end of the meal, George began discussing our Cost Project, his early concern for the anti-Semitism in what I called the "Al Calligan Affair." I was very careful to say little or express opinions about any Saco-Lowell personnel. He then asked about some of his colleagues and had quite a few stories that began, "Did you know that . . . ?" Again I was careful *not* to express my opinions. Finally he asked about our various personnel in the office, Grace, Priscilla, etc and asked, "Did you know that Charlie Crogan once played for the New York Yankees?"

I chuckled and said, "Yes. Great story!"

He continued, "You know, I think I saw batting practice the day that he got hurt!"

"No! You didn't! What a coincidence!" I exclaimed.

As we were walking to the car after dinner, he asked, "And what do you know about 'your girl, Lennie'?"

I was half-way expecting that question in view of Grace's recent alert so was quite prepared in saying, "Not very much! She was screened by our Personnel Department, and I accepted Rusty Dennett's decision to try her on this special project. Since she'd been an earlier Saco-Lowell employee and was a friend of Priscilla's, he thought she'd fit in quickly. And time was of the essence as you know."

I did not know whether or not he knew what I knew about their dating and her shaky marital situation. Nor did I give him a clue.

Driving home at sunset, we discussed the beauty of the ocean and pastel-tinted cumulus on the horizon. Since Maryllyn and I were tired and had heavy family commitments on Saturday and Sunday, we didn't invite them to come in for coffee.

I got up early to reach the Shops at eight o'clock on Saturday; played a few moments with Donna, hitched a ride to town with my sister Nancy since it was her Saturday turn to work at the bank. At the office I did some routine paper work until noon, then rode my bike down dusty and gravely West Street to Curtis Cove, arriving just in time for a quick sandwich and a change of clothes to grab clam hoe and baskets to hit the two-fifteen o'clock low tide. Maryllyn had already left Donna with her mom, had reached Little River and had dug half a basket full before I hit the flats. Together we dug about a bushel and a half. What fun, no matter how tough on our back muscles! The sun was bright, and the surface of the river glistened as it trickled through the flats. We talked incessantly, discussed the rippled sand on the flats and watched the minnows for which a few scattered terns occasionally dived. I even resorted to the 4"x6" pad I usually carried in my hip pocket to scribble a few notes I'd forgotten to jot down and to write one haiku:

> Where do clamworms go
> at high tide when gulls wing home,
> nature tooth and claw . . .

Barely surviving while crossing the green-headed, fly-laden marsh and fresh from a shower at Maryllyn's folk's home, we shucked clams for dinner and made our quota for supplying some of our Saco & Biddeford friends (customers)! All of us were struggling to make due with our rationed food stamps; also we were continuing to save for our Graduate School fund. (Also, I had begun to wonder how many Harvard students had dug clams to pay tuition?) As always, exercise in fresh salt air worked its magic; sleep came quickly.

Since mom and dad had seen little of Donna, the three of us accepted a Sunday dinner invitation or urging to visit This gave Maryllyn a break from both kitchen and hospital nursing; both of us had been eating, "catch as catch can," so the change at both parents' homes was more than welcome.

Our discussion at Hutchins Street in Saco pivoted mostly around Donna's care at Curtis Cove, dad's Saco-Lowell inspection job, Maryllyn's and my work lives at the hospital and Saco-Lowell. Also, mother was still doing laundry for some of Saco's wealthiest families so she had brocade shirts and underclothes laid or hung out to dry and press in various parts of the house.

We all talked at high speed so each of us was trying to "get words in edgewise!" Maryllyn shared details about some of her nursing duties and procedures. Since I tended to talk too much anyway, it was a more important that I listen. Dad was full of enthusiasm for his job despite the fact that the Sylvania "cans" (part of anti-submarine depth bombs) were still cutting his hands "unmercifully." He had, however, resigned himself to using thick leather gloves when handling the sharp edges of those aluminum tubes that were allegedly designed to hold the ammunition or fuses. Mother was enthusiastic about the dollars rolling in to help them pay taxes, both on their home and for their rustic cottage at Ossipee Lake, as well as routine expenses. Dad also pitched in to point out that he was still doing a little automobile repair "on the side" but refusing to work on cars where he'd not get paid. With most people now doing war work, however, their own economic depression seeming to be a thing of the past.

Looking plaintively at mother, he said, "And I occasionally get money from old debts!"

Mother continued eating but didn't look up, remarking, "Thank heaven!"

I realized that it would happen sooner or later, but eventually dad asked, "And how did you make out getting doors for the shops' johns?"

I knew that I needed to be careful in answering that question because gossip was cheap both at the shops and at home. So I fudged a little and said, "I'm optimistic about it, dad, but don't have all the details worked out. We should know in another week or so. But thanks for asking and keeping your eyes open. It was a good question for you to raise."

"I understand," he said, his eyes tearing up.

After hugs and good byes, we drove to the nearest gasoline station in town, Maryllyn "spending" her last ration tickets that would last us until the next ones came in at the end of the month. By the time we had taken Donna to her other grandmother's and returned to our rented attic room, we were ready to call it a day.

12. OPEN DOORS AND HOT IRON

When Priscilla and I sat down in what I'd come to call "The Conference Room," I asked if I could get her a cup of coffee. She declined, indicating that she had to get started on the work sheets and blueprints for the Drawing frame we were costing out.

"As I understand it, we send Don Goldman to start Drawing machines tomorrow."

"Yeah, that's right so I hope this won't take long."

I opened our conversation: "I've read your report and as I understand it, there's a total of twenty-four women's and twenty men's toilets out there in the shops and a total of ten women's and eight men's here in the offices. And in the shops all but four of the women's rest rooms have stalls with doors whereas there are only two men's stalls with doors; but here in the offices all but one has closed stalls for both women and men. Is my understanding correct?"

Priscilla referred to her own charts, said, "Right."

"So much for numbers, did you talk with any of the workers, men or women?"

"Yes. In every instance with the women, they resented having open doors, said that it was embarrassing. About half the men with open doors said the same thing; one reported that his constipation made him sick, literally. They all mentioned the stink."

"In short, sister, the system is generally abhorred by the users?"

"Yes!"

"And would you call it generally discriminatory?"

"Well, Roy, I'm not a men's or a women's suffragette, but, yes, I guess it is when you come to think of it!"

"Well, you know Mark Black as well as I do, what do you think his reaction will be when I take this report to him?

"Look, Roy, I don't want to get into trouble. . . ."

"No, he won't blame you for a condition that exists. I'll take any blame that may be handed out, and I don't know how the Union will 'come down with it' in the shops. In short, please don't worry about that aspect of things. It would be my guess that management, whoever that is, will play it quietly. Nobody wants to stir up a hornets nest during a war!"

As she left the room, she exclaimed, "I'll say not!"

Deciding to check with Black before I got tied up with something else, I drifted by his office, knocked, went in, asked if he had a minute. He was pleasant and more or less relaxed so I sat down opposite his table-like desk. I spent five or so minutes explaining my mission and reviewing the numbers in Priscilla's report. He listened carefully. When I was through, he asked how I happened to get into the topic. I reminded him about dad's coming to me with the problem.

"Well, I've known your father all my life and I trust his judgment. We've 'gotta' do something."

"Mr. Black," I continued, "I have a suggestion. I'm sure we don't want to cause a big fuss, and we surely will if the Union gets involved. How about a direct order from Kettley's or your office to have the sheet metal and wood-processing departments team up to design and make the simplest type of door and install them gradually over a month or so period. I'm sure you know of some account within the Shops Maintenance budget to handle such an item. And, if this request comes directly from you and/or Kettley, it seems to me that the employees will quickly appreciate the change and hence there would be no crisis. The job would be completed before it became a Union or some other kind of issue."

"Good thinking, Roy," he concluded. "I'll start the project first thing tomorrow. I'll only involve the two superintendents."

I started to leave his office when he said, "Do you have time to talk about your future now?"

"There's always plenty to do, but if you've time, let's talk." He leaned back in his swivel chair, reached for some notes that he'd evidently prepared for the conversation. He began, "I know that we'd talked before you headed for Bates, and that you proved me wrong. . . . "

I interrupted, "No, Mr. Black, I don't think you were wrong in attempting to dissuade me; you had lots of good arguments. As you know, it's been tough financially, especially when we tried to borrow money to accelerate my Bates program to graduate early. But you may have underestimated my determination? Furthermore, you found work for me all those college years, and Maryllyn and I have been grateful. . . . "

He then interrupted me. "Well, let's go on. As I understand it, you want to go on to get a PhD so you can teach at the college level?"

"Yes, sir, some of my Bates professors urged me to do it because they thought I could. So I am prepared psychologically."

"But could you defer it, build up your savings, and get some teaching experience?" he asked.

"Almost impossible to get into college teaching with only a Bachelor's degree, or even a single Master's degree. Also, I have to begin to publish; and as my Bates counselors say, that's the 'currency of the realm' or it's 'publish or perish'!'"

Black continued, "OK, I'm not up to date on all that, but let me tell you what I see as your future here. It should be obvious to you that you succeed in everything you do; you proved it in the runner-boy job when you arrived, you proved it in the Contracts and Specs work, also in Tool Coordinating and Terminations. And from all I can tell, the Cost Project is going well under your direction. Naturally, I heard about your handling of the Al Calligan and John MacScott cases. And you've just handled the open-door john situation diplomatically. Surely, you understand that."

Getting fidgety, I started, "Just but . . . "

"Hear me out, Roy. I want to tell you what I see ahead. Many of the foremen that I supervise will be retiring. We'll need somebody to replace them. Also awhile back you spoke of becoming a salesman or even an erector like your Uncle Frank. On any of those jobs you'd earn two to ten times what you're now making. And doing that without the sacrifices you and Maryllyn will have to make if you go on to get a Doctor's degree. In short, I think that the world of Saco-Lowell is wide open to you to make of it what you will." He went on to share some financial charts he'd made about the possibilities. I agreed with the statistics with which he presented his arguments.

I debated with myself as to what to say. Maryllyn and I had discussed it repeatedly and came back to her question each time, "Roy, what do *you* want to do?"

I related this dialogue to Black, told him that I respected his viewpoint and his concern for me and my family. That I would run over the matter again with Maryllyn, but that "I still think I want to try the challenge of the academic world before settling into the industrial one."

He leaned back in his chair, smiled, then remarked, "Once you make up your mind, you're a tough customer for holding your ground!"

I smiled, too, and said, "I'll think some more about it as October 25 rolls around," then asked, "Mr. Black, have we done any thinking about the situation if we don't quite finish the Cost Project and somebody has to come in and pick up the reins to see it through?"

"No, because I've been hoping you would stay to complete the job or might be willing to defer your leaving for a later semester at Harvard."

"The latter might work, although our housing situation in the Cambridge area has to be finalized pretty quickly. I think that we'd better begin making plans for my successor."

"Do you have any suggestions?" he asked.

"Yes, I've run it through my head. I think that Freddie Cote, John Barlows' assistant in the Cost Department would do a good job."

Black picked up the thread of thought, said, "Good choice; I know Freddie, and he's a good man to work with. Let's talk more about it. Thanks for our conversation. I hope you'll reconsider."

"Thank you, sir," and I left for my office, both elated for holding my ground and yet continued to feel somewhat torn.

Back at my desk, I answered a couple of routine questions from Grace and Priscilla and acknowledged Joe Ainsley's presence in the engineers' corner space. He nodded back and I held out my hands, palms upward, as though to ask, "Any news?" He shook his head in the negative.

I reconfirmed my appointment with the Top Roll supervisor the next morning, Tuesday. I told Grace my intentions in light of having talked half the morning and feeling a need to walk a bit that I'd decided to stroll down to the foundry to visit Wade Hansen, a TA grad who'd worked in the shops since graduating from Thornton. He had asked me to drop by whenever I had a moment so that he could "show me the ropes."

I caught him setting up a new mould at his station not too far from the blast furnaces.

"Hi, Wade," I greeted him, "How 'ya doin' and 'gotta' spare moment?"

He turned, held out his sandy hand, and returned my greeting. I stepped to his bench and asked if he would run through his routine so I could see if I could follow his procedure. Within seconds he was clamping the steel mould shut and beginning to fill it with sand, only stopping to insert the pattern of a six-inch pulley for the top of a carding machine. Once he told me what it was, I didn't need further identification. He was so muscular and in such great shape, he didn't need many moves to complete the task and set the finished mould onto the foundry's dirt floor and reach for the next mould and the next. He made a half dozen while I was watching his smooth body motions. I expressed admiration for his deft movements, then expressed an opinion: "Wade, you do this so smoothly, how many years have you been doing it?"

"Eleven-plus," he replied.

"And how long does it take for an apprentice to reach this stage of competence?"

"Three or four years."

"And does Bedaux,'s time-study check you out often?"

"Oh, about every six months or so, especially if I beat standards too soon or by too many moulds."

"In short, if you beat the system?"

"Yeah, or push it too hard."

"So, does this make it tempting to slow down when the time-study folk come down from their penthouse perches on the Biddeford Shop to check your standards?"

"Sure, we're always watching our production so as not to get too far ahead of the standards and make too much extra money in any given week!"

I chuckled.

"You know, Roy, that the managers don't want to pay us too much. That's what and why the unions are trying to monitor the repressive forces of our efforts. You probably know that from reading about the early time-studies in the Pittsburgh steel mills."

"Yeah, I did read about that in an elementary economics course at Bates, called the Taylor system as I recall, but I hadn't heard any of this from "the horse's mouth.""

"Or a horse's ass, like me," Wade joked.

"Come on, man! But seriously, this kind of tug of war must go on throughout the shops."

"Of course, and it always comes up at union meetings!"

"OK, but tell me, Wade, how do you personally handle or manage the pouring of the red hot, molten iron and the constant noises from the cranes overhead?"

"The noise is easy. I sometimes wear earplugs so I can hear myself think. The molten iron is another thing. Make a single slip against the iron pots and you're in for some nasty blisters . . . or let a drop of it spill onto your feet and you're in trouble. That's why we wear those asbestos leggings you've seen most days when they're pouring the iron. Some of those sparks that fly about are not as harmless as they may look. In other words you have to be on your toes. That's why we're paid a differential hourly rate for the two kinds of work. But it's damned dangerous at best."

"Yeah, I understand; that's why I avoid walking through here when you're pouring and go around via the longer way between the Biddeford Shops and the office."

"Damned smart, Roy; keep it up and you may live to be a hundred and not to 34, like the guy who got killed here the other day!"

"Yeah, I read about it in the *Journal*, a guy with wife and two small children. Let me ask one other question, Wade, although you may have already answered it. Why do you suppose Kettley is so slow, maybe even reluctant to feed me overhead percentages for this operation so we can cost out the foundry as part of this huge Cost Project we've got going?"

Wade quietly looked around as though to check if anybody was watching or listening, then spoke in lower tones than he had up to this point. I hastily interjected, "Don't answer me if you feel compromised, Wade; I don't want to get you in trouble."

"No, it's OK. My honest answer is, 'I don't really know.' You'll probably have to ask him for the real reason. Our foundry foreman refuses to discuss this issue when he's come to our union meetings. I can speculate that it has something to do with the wide range of functions that molders and pourers such as myself have to perform. It requires different ranges of skill as compared with what machinists do on lathes, drill presses, metal cutters, etc. Except for doing multiple moulds for the same part or multi-patterned moulds where we might do a half dozen pieces of the same part, there's little repetitive motion, hence time-checking is more complex. Also, the matter of wasted materials related to faulty constructing of moulds, different weather conditions when we pour, winter-versus-summer for instance, and so on. But these are speculations; you'll have to speak about it to the big man upstairs. I doubt if our foreman can answer your fundamental question because he's more of an expert on handling men and molten iron than the fine points of accounting."

Noting it was almost noon, I told Wade that I hoped I'd not broken his intent to "break standards today," thanked him, shook his sandy hand, and returned to the office tossing "next projects" around in my head like the proverbial juggler!

But back at the office, Grace informed me that I had a confirmed appointment with the Top Roll Department the next morning. I spent the balance of that afternoon reviewing the more complex parts' sheets which Grace and Priscilla claimed were illegible, especially the identification of the machine tools on which the parts were made. We were deep into the project and needed to move away from the old problem of the six wise men trying to identify the elephant by way of his or her disparate parts!

13. TOP ROLLS AND BOTTOM LINES

It was with some fear and trepidation that I approached work today. I had to face a shop foreman regarded as the most powerful in the shop. I mulled over the reasons why I may have avoided him; nor could I be sure that Joe Ainsley hadn't discussed my omission with some of his colleagues about this seeming avoidance. But, anyway, as I checked in with Grace to see if there were any problems, phone calls and office issues, I could feel my tendency to procrastinate whenever my imagination ran wilder than my logic. Maybe, I hunched, I'm simply putting off the inevitable for all the wrong reasons.

I stopped by the time clock and noted that Joe hadn't checked in so I asked myself, "Was he also practicing avoidance?" I quickly looked in to say hello to both the Electrical Department's Ken Trendholm and the Snagging Department's Charlie Gendron, assuring them that I'd be back to answer any questions they might have; also waved to Wade Hansen in the Foundry and yelled a "Thank you!" for his help. Finally reached the third floor on the Biddeford Shops and strode into the top roll office with more exterior confidence than I felt.

"Mornin', Mannie," I said in holding out my hand. Though Mannie had been known to refuse to shake with "office folk," he smiled and shook hands firmly. We passed the time of day. His second hand, Art Remilard, hands black with machine grease,

95

came in from repairing an "ancient" lathe, washed his hands and shook his own hand ("sorta mucked up!" he explained, smiling). We all "shot the breeze" regarding the Red Sox's game the night before on radio. In short, we seemed to start the visit on a light note.

Finally, I asked, "How's Joe Ainsley doing on the Cost Project? I see that he's not checked in this morning."

Mannie and Art exchanged glances, then Mannie spoke up, "Yeah, he phoned a little while ago, said he might not be in today, said you would probably know why."

I scowled a little, then explained. "He might have tried to get me at the office, but I can only speculate why he might be absent."

Mannie continued, "Something about having to spend the day on the phone with New York."

"Oh, that!" I remarked. "His family has some kind of problem with the law, I don't know the details." I didn't tell them, but I drew a little inner sigh of relief, fearing he might be under interrogation with the Saco police at that very moment.

Mannie spoke up as though it relieved him, then went on. "You know, Art and I 'kinda' like the guy. He's smart, not only converses well but after a couple of weeks here, he fit right in, enjoys morning coffee with Art and me. Although he doesn't know all of our crew, he talks and jokes with them, gets a kick out of the fact that the men have pet names for some of their machines, laughs when they talk or swear at their favorite machines as though they were animal pets. We don't know if he's getting all of the information you need for the Cost Project, but he's not afraid to ask our opinions when a question comes up. And he sure does understand the machinist trade. But tell us, Roy, are you getting the information you need in order to do what Kettley and Black intend to do with government agencies?"

I replied in the affirmative, assuring them that I'd studied his parts sheets and they seem to be both precise and comprehendible.

In unison Art and Mannie responded, "Great!" Mannie continued, "We sure are behind the project because we certainly do not want to lose our jobs for failing to get relief from the Office of Price Administration."

"Nor do I," and I paused, then went on, "I think you can help me a little by running a couple of things past me. When I first came into the shops in 1936, I heard draftsmen and engineers talk again and again about the revolution they might be creating by improving the materials for top roll coverings, finding more durable "stuff;" but they rarely said anything about bottom rolls. I know you have some model set-ups here; in fact, they've been sitting around since I used to run all over the shops correcting specifications and lists of parts even in the middle of textile mill contracts. In fact, they were set up very much as you have them there." (I pointed to a bench in their office). "In short could you explain, maybe for the tenth time what's happening and tell me in layman's terms?"

Both men smiled then beckoned me to visit their models.

Mannie began, "I assume you know that the bottom rolls on most machines are steel."

"I do."

"And that the grooves in those rolls are cut unevenly so they'll assist but not resist cutting the yarn as it passes over them."

"O.K. I'm following."

Mannie went on, "For eons or at least decades, the top rolls were covered with leather so as to grip the yarn as it passed between top and bottom rolls. Well, leather was fine when it was new, but as it wore from the yarn passing over it repeatedly, hour after hour, day after day, week after week, the leather tended to lose its gripping power; and you'll recall that some of the rolls were turning at different speeds to draw out the thread even as it twisted from the thread moving sidewise as well as between top and bottom rolls. " He paused a moment, then asked, "Are you with me?"

"Yes, please go on!"

"Well, for years our engineers, using trial and error methods, tried to locate materials that improved the performance of leather."

"Wood, cloth, etc.?"

"Yes, although cloth covers simply lying on top of each bay and pulled down by gravity, did help some."

"So, that's why these synthetic plastic rolls are now substituted for all other materials?"

Yes! Mannie explained, and Art grinned as they jointly manipulated the small demonstration models on their bench and added, "That's about where we are now, but the research folk are still experimenting. And, of course, how well or poorly the process works depends upon many variables. Our job here in the shop is to follow their specifications as closely as possible. The so-called "Biddeford fit" will not work in this environment where tolerances are so much closer than they used to be when Art and I started in this department a decade or so ago." Art nodded as he grinned.

"So?" I queried, "Are you continuing to modify the processes at both the machine level and synthetic adaptation levels? And how do you order these synthetics?"

Art spoke up, saying, "Since that's my major responsibility, I have to deal with the variances when the 'plastic tubes' (what I call them) come in from companies like Dupont. I think that they are getting closer and closer to our needs. We don't have so many rejects as we slip the top roll tubes on over the machine bases. . . . "

We were interrupted by a phone call, Grace trying to reach me. Joe Ainsley was at the office, asking to see me as soon as possible., asked me to come right back! "It's crucial." I said, "OK," and turned to Mannie and Art, lifted my eyebrows and said, "Joe Ainsley's at the office and asked if I could come back immediately, it's something about the law! So I guess I've 'gotta' go."

"Hope Joe's OK," Mannie remarked. "Keep us informed, Roy?"

"As much as possible unless it's confidential."

"We understand," they said in unison.

I thanked them for their demonstration, promised to be in touch, and began walking toward the office, musing about Joe's difficulty and wondering how much of that I must be concerned about?

When I got to the office, I said hello to each of the staff working at their Frieden calculators, tapped Charlie Crogan on the shoulder, asked, "How did the Yankees do last nite?"

He replied, "Won of course!" He smiled and I scowled as I looked toward my desk. No Joe in sight, but Grace soon apprised me that she assumed it was confidential so she'd put him in our informal "conference room." I moved unobtrusively to that room, tapped on the door window as he looked up. Entered.

"Hi, Joe, how 'ya' doing?"

"I've been 'bettah' as your Maine kinfolk say!"

I chuckled, sat down and asked, "Yes, what is it?"

"Roy, I'll save you lots of words, but my worst fears now threaten to choke me! The Saco police want to interrogate me this afternoon. Will you go with me as a character witness to verify my story?"

"But, Joe, I hardly know you."

"But you know me better than anybody else in this part of Maine."

"That's probably true, but . . . "

"But I need you! I swear. Never been in this kind of situation before."

I looked at him, looked at the floor and out the window, asked "Did they tell you why they wanted to talk with you?"

"Not really, something about a rape and involvement with my colleague here."

This led to a discussion about Pete and the ethics of informing upon him as well as time for Joe's being off the Cost Project at least another half day. I told Joe that Mannie and Art at the Top Roll job seemed to like him, and we reviewed the situation for most of an hour. Since we both had our lunches with us, we munched while we talked. Finally, I said, "It may not be my better judgment, but I'll go with you."

We needed to be there by two o'clock. I was not dressed very formally, but did have a light suit coat and a tie at the office. He, too, so we'd be presentable.

I felt a bit nervous, but Joe's lying awake half the night began to show. In the time left before leaving, I encouraged him to try to relax on the old folding camp cot that I kept handy for quick naps.

Following life-long advice of a lawyer friend, I advised him to answer only questions asked him and *not* to volunteer more information than that for which they asked. At 2: 15 PM we went to his car and headed for the Saco Police Department in Saco City Hall.

14. RAGGED EDGES OF THE LAW

We reached the police station behind Saco City Hall, were greeted by a clerk who escorted us to a rather barren room furnished only with table and chairs. Shortly thereafter, two rather burly uniformed policemen entered somewhat belligerently, announced their names as Pete Lemaine and Art Tardiff, shook hands rather formally. Asked our names, then sat.

The younger of the two men spoke up and asked, "Didn't you go to Bates?"

I answered in the affirmative and began to place him in my gallery of acquaintances.

"And you graduated from Thornton?"

"Yes."

"You were a football manager who taped ankles . . ." at which point I said, "And you are the Art Tardiff, who played halfback at TA, but left Bates before the football season had hardly begun?"

"You got it," and he extended his hand to shake again. Joe looked on with mouth agape, but it was clear that the place might be a bit more friendly than if this acquaintance hadn't been acknowledged.

I felt the urge to build on this recognition, but the older officer, Pete Lemaine, cut in to ask, "And why are you here, Mr. Fairfield?"

"Because Joe asked me to come as a character witness; he's working with me on a cost project at Saco-Lowell."

"And how long have you been at Saco-Lowell?"

"Almost six years over an eight-year period."

A short-hand specialist had joined us by this time and was recording the conversation.

Lemaine turned to Joe, said, "This is only an informal meeting. No charges have been filed. But I must tell you that notes from this meeting might be used if a lawsuit arises, so the transcript had better reflect the truth. Do you both understand that?"

We answered in the affirmative.

Then began a long and rather torturous dialogue where I served primarily as witness with virtually no input. Lemaine asked most of the questions, and Joe presented virtually the same picture as he'd painted for me the previous week. Finally Lemaine turned to me and asked, "Is this essentially as you understand it?"

"Yes, sir," I responded.

He then got into Pete's end of the story. Did Joe know me? Had he discussed the matter with me? Did his wife know anything about his visit to the prostitute? Had he heard from the young woman since the violent scene? Joe was straightforward with his answers and did not stray off on irrelevant tangents.

I watched Art Tardiff's eyes bouncing around the room and occasionally off mine, exchanged one or two smiles with me although I listened very intensely lest I miss a subtlety of question or answer.

Finally, Lemaine turned to me. "Mr. Fairfield, did you know that Saco and Biddeford had a house of ill repute?"

"Not for sure, although years ago, I heard some of the roughhouse visitors to my dad's garage on Hutchins Street joke

102

about it. But I was never sure whether it was for real or a product of those 'tough-guys' imaginations."

"Did they ever say where it was?"

"They mentioned two places, one down town where Joe says he was, and another at the foot of Dean's Hill, in the block near the bridge. But that was fifteen or so years ago."

"Did those men whom you refer to as 'tough-guys' ever discuss the legality or illegality of such a house?"

"Not that I remember, but I doubt if they would have known. Their off-color stories and jokes were part of what I came to realize as 'a culture of filth' and it turned me off.

"College purity?" Tardiff quipped.

I started to react, but backed away from it, trying to practice the counsel I'd given Joe.

"In short," Lemaine continued, "you have no hard knowledge about this place alleged to be downtown, nor know of anybody associated with it?"

"That's true, Mr. Tardiff."

"And what about you, Joe, have you told us the full story? Was this incident part of your style of living or just a impulsive reaction to your wife's behavior?"

"The latter," Joe responded in a clipped manner.

About a half hour had passed then Lemaine asked his colleague, "Do you have anything more to ask or say?"

"No sir," the subordinate responded.

As the two officers dismissed us, I said, "You know, Art, I have one more question. "

"What's that?"

"I vaguely remember that you had a wide and fairly flat ankle, a joy to tape. Do you still?"

Art lifted up his pant leg. I studied it for a moment, then remarked, "Just as I remembered. If you ever need another tape job, come see me! I've not forgotten those skills." We parted laughing!

Returning to the Shops, Joe and I exchanged views of the meeting with the cops. Joe thought that it was quite "lucky" that Art Tardiff remembered me quite positively despite the one snide remark about college purity. I expressed the view that Lemaine had behaved quite properly and opined that Joe would never hear from the case again. I urged him to return to his Thatcher Hotel room, take a nap, eat a solid dinner and I'd see him in the morning.

And as we parted, I said, "Joe, the guys on the Top Roll job like you. But I'd be inclined to shuffle off any 'explanation' with some off-hand remark such as 'Oh, nothing too serious, just family business.' No point in putting any grist into the rumor mills!"

He nodded, "Good advice."

15. SNAGGING AND SHOCKING

Away from desk and office needs for much of yesterday, I decided to bear down on the summary sheets which Grace and Priscilla could not process for lack of information or glitches in machine tool numbers. Luckily I didn't have too many interruptions although the Textile Repair folk called me to the Specification Department files, which I once maintained, to help clarify a machine number for a Springs Cotton Mills contract . . . a mild bump in the road.

Returning through the Drafting Room, however, I got sidetracked by Elwood Giles, Chief of Drafting with whom I had climbed Mt. Evans in the tough Mahoosuc Range just east of Mt. Washington. He wanted to report on a recent hike over Mt. Lafayette in the Presidential Range. He showed me a few slides via a hand-viewing machine he kept in his office. Also, he wanted to know if my schedule might include a trip to Katahdin in September.

Hated to do so, but told him my time would be tight as we wound down this Cost Project and I prepped for graduate school in late September. We talked a bit about that, and he said he agreed with Mark Black that I should stay with Saco-Lowell rather than going for a doctorate. I thanked him for his vote of confidence; then we talked a little about the crew of mechanical engineers with whom I was working. He admitted that they had been pleasant and fairly quiet and had only approached his men a few times for technical information.

Back at the office I was available to respond to a few phone calls from foremen, but there were no serious questions. Also, worked with Grace and Priscilla in an effort to smooth out some minor snags in the engineers' cost sheets. I then carried a folder full of the most troublesome sheets into the quiet of the conference room; also for the first time in what seemed like weeks, I carried my copy of Mann's *The Magic Mountain* along with my lunch. I hoped for a three or four -hour retreat from routine to work on cost sheets dealing with assemblies and subassemblies. I knew that Grace could handle most of the routine "stuff!"

The planning was fortuitous, and I did work on cost processes except for forty-five minutes of reading about Hans Catsorp's "magic mountain," a perspective that altered the meaning of his effort to outlive tuberculosis pressures and implications. As he adjusted to conditions at the sanatorium high in the mountains, returning to every day life seemed to be less meaningful. One could hardly escape the symbolism, and I tried to put myself into Catsorp's skin and psyche, which I supposed was part of what Thomas Mann was trying to do.

The book reminded me of what one of my English professors told us at Bates, "Stick with your metaphors! Stick with your metaphors!" In fact, years later, when I got heavy into poetry, a close Saco friend encouraged the same course of thought and I ran that sentence through my mind and my writing many times before getting the full message.

On that particular day at Saco-Lowell, the climate was just humid enough for dozing in the hot sun streaming through the mullioned windows cutting up the landscapes into many tiny-framed rectangular pieces, chunks of an azure sky and red-bricked, mill buildings. My dozing was briefly shattered as

Priscilla knocked on the door gently, broke in briefly to report that she'd had lunch with dad over on the Ford job and he was tickled that somebody "had put doors on his rest room stalls." We joined in giggling satisfaction about that problem having been solved fairly quietly! As she started back to the office, she laughed, "It's not what you know but *who* ya' know!" I nodded!

When I reached a time to break for the day, I carried all my papers back to the office, conferred with Priscilla and Grace regarding the inclusion/integration of my work with theirs, and touched base with several of the mechanical engineers as they headed for the time clock at the end of the Drafting Room. Also helped Charlie Crogan with a mathematical problem and joshed him about the Yankees being defeated the day before. He laughed and said, "It's a rare day goes by I don't think what might have been!"

I responded, "Well, you could imagine that this room is Yankee Stadium and you've become a baseball statistician, now married to a Frieden calculator!" He headed for home, tossing a "Yea-ah" over his left shoulder.

Before Grace left, I outlined the next day's schedule, indicating that I was going to try to visit both the Snagging and Electrical Departments the same morning since they were close by. She responded, "See you at noon. Will phone you if a storm breaks out!"

Once punching in the next day and cursing the "misfortune" of being chained to a time clock, I stepped around the corner into the Snagging Room. It was run by Dick Winguarard, a man who claimed publicly that he'd "eaten a ton of cast iron dust." I wasn't sure about the wisdom or lack of it in making such a claim. But nobody could possibly enter that tiny department, no more than thirty-feet square and boasting three rows of grinders in bays of four-foot square each, to say nothing about a similar number of parts boxes on wheels, which had to be rolled in and out of the department, between machines and a rickety old elevator connecting them with the Foundry. Nobody could possibly stick a nose into that place without feeling suffocated by the dust-laden air, nor being deafened by those high-speed grinders where they processed hundreds of iron castings smoothing them down to their specified sizes or shapes every day.

The entire procedure meant more care on the part of the grinders than might first meet the eye as the operators snapped off the balance of the tube-like channels via which the molten iron made its way to the spaces where the patterns filled the moulds. Although the preliminary shaping of the castings eliminated the worst of the iron clinging to each textile part, still there was much shaping to be done. Although there was an effort to keep the air clean via blowers and suction fans, still it was a filthy and dangerous place to work. The grinders were exposed to motor drives or overhead belts, always a hazard to get a hand or arm hooked into a fast-moving part. Also, even wearing masks and heavy gloves to protect their faces and hands, the men were still exposed to sharp edges on the parts being cleaned up for later machining. In short it was a very dangerous job in the pre-NOAH era . . . even though the Union attempted, quite unsuccessfully, to control cleaning up the work environment.

At the end of any given day, one could stand beside the stream of men (women rarely took that job!) streaming home through the gates and tell fairly quickly who had worked in the Snagging Room that day.

At one point in my early employment at Saco-Lowell, I had been jokingly threatened by one department supervisor to "shape up or go to the Snagging Room," so I had studied the conditions there and even tried snagging for an hour one day long before the Cost Project took me there. Naturally enough the Cost engineers were not begging to go there themselves so we arranged to have a special glassed-in "cage" available when they had to "follow" the production process of specific parts.

The foreman, Dick Winguarard, was a nice guy. He understood the fact that the snaggers made a good living wage if they worked their butts off, developed seniority, and managed to keep breathing, not easy since black lung was by no means confined to the coal-mining industry in West Virginia. On the day I appeared in the snagging room, I asked Dick how he and the engineer were getting along.

He was honest, admitted that he didn't envy Harry Golden's job, but felt that he'd been cooperative. He understood his snaggers' resentments about the glass-caged observation spot where the engineers were sheltered from all the hazards of the work place whereas they were not. "But," Dick explained, "we do what we must do and 'damn' the consequences! We got here by hard, dirty work. I hope that our participation helps us survive. Give my regards to Mark Black, he helped me get started ten years ago."

I assured him that I would speak to Mark, then I swung around the corner to the Electrical Department.

Bill Moore happened to be at his desk, rather odd, too, because he "sorta" wore two hats: he and his crew kept the shops' electrical circuits with all their complexities in good repair so that all the employees in the plant could continue working in the event of black-out emergencies such as thunder showers knocking out the power.

His second responsibility was that of wiring each of the textile machines shipped all over the world. These procedures were developed when the Biddeford, Newton and Kitson (Lowell) plants were consolidated in Biddeford and Saco in the Twenties. Fortunately, the textile mills in the area had generated a fairly large number of first-rate electricians.

Fortunately for me, my father-in-law, Jesse Rumery, was one of those local persons who got in on the ground floor when electricity became the power source for running both machine tools and the textile machines shipped to the world. Jesse spent many hours relating details as well as conducting me through the steam plant at the foot of Deans and York Hills, across from the York Mfg Co . . . the one with the 200-foot smoke stack (around the top of which Jesse boasted he had walked . . . and had photos to show it!). I never felt comfortable around all the switches in the powerhouse, nor watching Jesse fill the building with sparks and heavy crackling sounds as he switched hundreds and thousands of volts from one line to another, depending upon demand! So I pretty much understood some of the pressures on Bill and his Electrical Department.

Today, I had a fairly practical problem related to the wiring of individual textile machines, most of which had some electrical gadget, switch, circuit breaker, stop motion, you name it, that was an intrinsic part of the functioning of those machines. Looking at the machines from a cost viewpoint, our cost engineers were not sure where the wire itself came in or went out. We designed our cost sheets to include those items supplied by our vendors; but we were not clear about the amount or nature of the wire that was part of the larger unit.

Bill looked up from his desk, smiled and observed, "You know, Roy, we've debated that issue for years. It's easy to see it both ways . . . or even a third way. First, make the solid split between the electrical units and the machine, charge the wire to the textile unit. Or secondly, vice versa; or thirdly, let the vendors send wire with their units. Frankly, I'd prefer that we were taken completely out of the loop and leave the decision to the erector and lump both wire and his time for cost purposes. Actually, it's a minor problem and I can live with it whichever way it goes."

"Bill, do you have any sense of which way it has been done in the past, that is, prior to the war? Supposedly, we're writing history."

Bill thought for a moment, then remarked, "Frankly, I don't remember, but suggest that we keep the wire tied as closely as possible to the machine, then that won't mess up our relationships with vendors where we have less control. Also, we can dictate our instructions to them."

About that time, the phone rang for me, so I thanked Bill and hastened to the office.

16. RUMOR RAGES RIFE & WHY!

When I got returned from another early morning trip to Packing
and Receiving, to clarify phone arrangements for an engineer's
visit, Grace was quick to announce Mark Black's wanting to see
me. It seems that rumor of a visit by President David Edwards
was being noised about and he wanted to see me . . . "as soon as
possible." So I retraced my steps toward his office, only to be
met by my old friend, Ralph Perry.

I shook hands and asked, "How're things?"

"OK, I guess, but rumor has it that David Edwards, Saco-
Lowell's distinguished president, had been seen downstairs
around Vice President Kettley's office . . . and you know, Roy,
what nerves that triggers."

"Yeah, I know the man, tall, lanky, usually dressed in gray
worsted, to match his hair."

"Remember how we used to send those comparisons of list
prices and selling prices which he was alleged to have used in
comptroller functions?"

"Do I ever remember . . . and never got a single word in
return!" I observed.

"Well!" Rex exclaimed, "So it's only another rumor that
he's around visiting. Probably nothing to it!"

"Let's hope, or at least nothing serious!" I fired back and
kept moving toward Mark Black's office.

Seeing Mark through his office window and starting to open the door a crack, Mark spoke up, "Come in, come in!"

"Grace said you were looking for me?"

"Yes, your old Saco friend, Lawrence Perry phoned awhile ago and informed me that President David Edwards was due for one of his own brands of inspection. He clued me that we'd better be prepared for a Progress Report on your Cost Project. We know how nervous Kettley is about that since we're investing so much money in it and it could be a craps shoot with the U.S. Government involved. Can you make such a report?"

"Does it need to be in writing or can it be oral?"

Mark smiled as he said, "Lawrence didn't say, but I suppose it wouldn't hurt if we had a page or two, something he can scan in fifteen seconds."

"OK, how much time do I have?"

"Oh, how about a half hour?" he smiled.

"Fine, but may I leave you with a question?"

"Yes?"

"Why do rumors fly so frequently fly around these offices and in the shops?"

"How many days do I have to comment on that one?" Black inquired, with an accompanying chuckle.

"That's up to you; I'll be back in half an hour." Mark was smiling again when I went thru the door.

Back at the office I took Grace into the conference room to dictate the report, figuring I had ten minutes and she would have twenty to transcribe her shorthand.

Looking at my watch, I quickly made an outline in my head and proceeded to "read" as Grace wrote. My major points:

Current date

Distribution of engineers in numbers of departments

Number of known parts processed

113

Types of problems encountered with the process
Hold-up as result of no overhead figures for Foundry
Types of ethnic issues encountered
Length of time we'd worked on project
Estimated time to the finish
Total cost to date

My timing turned out to be accurate and Grace's transcription was also within my estimate. Three copies in hand, I arrived back in Black's office in just thirty-three minutes. Mark's face was a wreath of grins, his wiry white eyebrows bouncing up and down as he congratulated me for accomplishing the chore.

I sat quietly as he scanned the report, timing him as he read it. As he laid the paper on his desk and turned, I glanced at my watch to report, "eighteen seconds!" He laughed heartily, then observed, "Just one thing I'd take out and one I'd modify."

"Which ones?" I inquired.

"Guess!"

"The ethnic issues and the question of Foundry overhead."

"To do what with which?" I asked

"Leave out the question of anti-Semitism and other ethnic intimidation; that mustn't be anywhere in print!"

"OK, I understand," then Black turned in his swivel chair looked out over the rooftops toward the Pepperell loom sheds, paused, a moment, then said, "Let's treat the Foundry overhead problem more gently. The way you've worded it might hurt Kettley, he's the CEO of this plant in his boss's eyes. We probably had best not risk it. I can speak with him privately about that issue."

"Fine with me, I countered, I'll have Grace revise the report. get it right back to you in case Edwards shows soon."

Black said "O.K. and if no emergency comes up, I'll discuss rumors at Saco-Lowell about four this afternoon."

"Super!"

Back at the office, Grace revised the report quickly, then walked it toward Mark's office where Ethel Bravard was filing. She was gone half an hour so I wondered what had happened.

Grace explained, "Black had gone down to Kettley's office. Strangest thing, Ethel was all excited about the prospects of President Edwards' showing up. And already an office pool was being organized with bets then going 5 to 3 against Edwards' coming. Nay-sayers had 'bin theyah befoah'!"

I laughed, especially when Grace asked, "Roy, do you think we should have our own pool or join with Specs and Parts to do our own betting?"

I responded with, "I don't especially believe in betting, always lose. But it's up to you if you want to call an office meeting and decide for yourselves."

Not much cost analysis got done during the next hour. Our office group agreed to join the other office group and by that time the Drafting Room had joined them so that by three o'clock about fifty were in the pool. It appeared to be as important as the World Series or a Thornton-Biddeford football game! They appointed an Edwards Watcher to patrol the offices and to contact several spotters in the factory and set the next day at five as the limit for the event to occur. Although I did not join the pool, Priscilla and Grace did.

In view of the five p.m. deadline the group had set for the end of the Edwards-Watch time, Mark Black postponed our discussion about rumors for a day and an hour. So I stepped into his office just as most of the workers were punching the time clock at the end of the Drafting Room. I could hear the "Clunk-Clunk" of the clock and the following bells ring as they lined up and left for home.

When stepping into Mark Black's office, I smiled just as he remarked, "So he didn't show!"

"No, but the nonevent sure did get a lot of attention. I'll bet that a bomb going off up on Main Street wouldn't have caused more commotion!"

"Probably not, but it might have been a morale builder because for a few hours everybody was on the same page. Not much different than betting on the World Series!"

"I suppose, but it didn't help much with our time lines for the Cost Project. But let's not dwell on it. I want to go back to my question about Saco Lowell rumors. I've never quite understood the phenomenon and would like your take. . . ."

Mark started to break in, but I interrupted . . .

"One more thing. Early in my Saco-Lowell experience, a day came along when a rumor flew around the Shops that Lou Gehrig had died. We tried to confirm it, even phoned Yankee stadium; unfortunately they were playing away and we couldn't reach anybody to check the news. In fact, not until the next day when the Yankees' box score was printed in the Portland papers did we see Gehrig's name right there batting clean-up in the Yankee line-up. I never knew what started the rumor. But why here? It seemed not to have happened at Pepperell or Bates Manufacturing!"

Black responded, "I recall the incident, and I remember how distraught you were. But I never got an explanation. But, your question as to why rumors start here is a good one."

"Thanks, Mr. Black, I'm beginning to think I'm nuts!"

"Not at all, but I think it's a good speculative question, and I do have thoughts about it, but no hard evidence," and he paused to take a deep breath. Then he continued: "Since the years of The Great Depression and the consolidation of the three factories in Massachusetts and Maine, our workers have felt a keen sense of insecurity, and I suppose that the appearance of David Edwards is a kind of omen which triggers and intensifies

116

that feeling. True, most people who work here are able to concentrate on what they're doing . . . at least enough so that too many limbs and lives are not lost to accidents. But even without tenure as in the academic world, about which you'll learn more if you become a college professor . . . and bless you if you do . . . one's job depends upon how many orders we get and how long the wheels turn on the gear job, or hammering sheets of copper in Saco's Slasher and Starching Department etc. You surely know the details.

"This morning I even phoned Rusty Dennett in Personnel and asked his opinion. Why does this happen? Russ couldn't explain it either. He did say that the war work makes many workers and new employees nervous about their future. They want work and they want the war to end, seemingly contradictory wishes. I floated my theory and he reminded me that President Edwards has a reputation for taking bold action, especially in the early days of The Depression and we nearly went under . . . "

I broke in, "But, Mr. Black, surely most S-L-S workers don't have many details about *that* part of our history. I've never had access to his notorious report to the stockholders in which he allegedly proposed strong medicine to heal an unhealthy corporation!"

"I agree, Roy. That's too logical and improbable a cause. I don't know. Maybe it's simply mass psychology?"

"Maybe," I surmised. Maybe we should try an experiment after things calm down and actually have Edwards show up someday, make some kind of announcement and see what happens!"

"Hey, Roy, do you want me to get fired? Despite my many years with the company, I'm in my fifties and need a job for a few more years until I can collect my pension!"

"Heavens no, I wouldn't want to jeopardize your job, and I need one for at least a couple more months!"

Black laughed, thanked me for coming in, and I ambled back to the Cost Project office.

But I noticed that this event-to-happen did *not* occur, the rumor and pool efforts surely did distract from everyday work. As I'd speculated once before, a bomb on Main Street, in either Biddeford or Saco, would probably have created no more rumor-mongering and excitement than this nonevent.

Also, I made a note to myself vowing to get my hands and eyes on that notorious Edwards' letter that he wrote to the Corporate members!

17. CAMBRIDGE INTERLUDE

When we'd nearly reached the half-way point between our starting the Cost Project and the time when I'd planned to leave for graduate school, Maryllyn and I thought it was an appropriate time to visit Cambridge to pin down our housing for late October even as I worked nearly sixty hours a week at Saco-Lowell. Somehow Maryllyn obtained some extra gasoline-rationed coupons, and we left for Boston at 5 o'clock on the following Saturday morning to look for an apartment. We were "armed" with rental agencies' names, newspaper ads, and a list of prospective apartments as well as cash for a down payment.

It was hot and with considerable tourist congestion in the York and Salisbury Beach areas on Route One, but it was the best way to go before the turnpike systems were built. Then, too, having driven to Fenway Park many times in the late Thirties, we knew the best way to avoid congested Boston traffic. So we pulled into the outskirts of the suburbs, took the lightly-traveled Felsway past the well-known Ford Motor assembly plant, and were soon sighting the Harvard residence houses on the Charles River.

At first we looked at two of the listed apartments on the Cambridge-Somerville line, but the areas looked run down and off the bus lines, so we looked at the buildings of a section of Cambridge closer to Harvard Yard. But there, as we expected, the prices were far beyond our range. So, one of the listed apartments on the first floor of a two-story house on Arlington Heights looked promising although it might mean a half-hour walk to take a bus to Harvard Square. Anyway, no harm looking and look we did, even to getting a casual "tour" via another student family who would be leaving, conveniently enough, by mid-October. The apartment was not especially well laid out, but we figured that it would be adequate. After all, Donna was only two and we would be leaving in three or four years. We talked with the owner who lived only a block or so away, signed the contract and put $84 down for two months beginning when the present students left. We scouted the route I would have to walk because we knew we could not afford a car and go to school simultaneously; also we reviewed the route to the nearest grocery market and taxi facilities on Mass Avenue. In short, we have so often thanked our "lucky stars" to have arranged all of this in such a short time, roughly five hours.

Since Maryllyn had never been in Harvard Yard, it seemed important to show her what little I knew about it, including Widener Library which would serve as my headquarters for the next three years. When we hit the road back to Maine in mid-afternoon, we looked at one another with amazement . . . to have done it so quickly and smoothly. It might have required many more trips if things hadn't bounced our way. As a result of this good fortune, we pulled into Maryllyn's folks' driveway at Curtis Cove just as the sun was setting deep red and the aviation signal light at Guinea and Oak Ridge Roads was beginning to flash on and off.

"Hot day tomorrow," I observed.

"Yeah, Roy, let's forget Saco-Lowell Shops and Trull Hospital, go fishing and clamming tomorrow!

"Agreed!" . . . as I gave her a "big hug."

Next morning we rowed the family dory a half mile beyond the mouth of Curtis Cove, "jigged" for harbor pollock, caught a dozen or so, fish enough for two or three meals for Maryllyn and both our families, despite the presence of the ever-pesky dog fish who got on the line easily enough but were difficult to shake off.

Fish, too, for Sunday lunch!

Then, the early afternoon tide was perfectly timed for us to dig six pecks of clams, carry them in a washtub up the green-headed-infested marsh, and shuck them for our families and in-town customers. We also had a quiet hour or so visiting my folks, checking on their physical condition and morale. Dad's hands were healing now that he was off the Sylvania "can job" and inspecting parts of the Ford bogey wheel castings. Mother kept on keeping on.

We needed no rocking to put us to sleep. Sunburns helped, too!

18. THE HIGH COST OF CERTAINTY

Monday morning came early but beautiful at Curtis Cove, ocean calm, lobstermen working their traps, crows cawing in the nearby pine and oak forest, gulls flapping their way south toward Kennebunkport. Much as I'd have loved to stay to be with Donna and Maryllyn for the day and as "criminal" it may have seemed to think about playing hooky, I knew that it was "back to the salt mine." Yet it didn't stop me from dreaming of the day when I would not be locked into tight schedules. Maryllyn, too, expressed similar wishes, but she had to leave for the hospital just as I needed to be at Saco-Lowell at 7 o'clock.

When we got up the dusty road to town, the dust in our teeth matched the grit we needed to face the day. She left me at the factory gate; I waved her a good-bye and wished the shop guards "good-morning" almost simultaneously. Grace and Priscilla were not in but a couple of the engineers were busy studying their cost sheets and the attached blueprints before heading for their departments. I merely "passed the time of day" in what I predicted was to be a hot and uncomfortable August day.

Once at the desk, I found Grace's, list of to-dos. At the top was a curt note: "Call Harry Sawyer about 'lost casting.'" I began calling him before reading further, because I could easily scan it while talking with Harry.

As I surmised, he was at his desk. "Grace said you called while I was away, Harry, what's new?"

"Army Ordinance is coming today. Can you be available at 10:30? I don't think it will take over a half hour."

"I'll be there, Harry." The next item: "Joe Ainsley wants to see you. Will arrive a little late so he can talk with you." I looked at my watch; it was 7:30. And so I went on scanning the list. Most items were routine. So I planned to stay in the office, "visit" with the staff, get back into the shops after lunch for some "*must visit.*" Meanwhile, I'd eat a quiet lunch with Mann's *The Magic Mountain* and try to get back to the threads of its dialogue.

Joe was true to his promise. He arrived a little late, suggested we move the exchange into our so-called Conference room.

Once settled, I inquired, "How's it going?"

"Not too bad, but I thought I owed it to you to bring you up to date regarding my marriage situation."

"It's not mandated, you know, Joe, although I appreciate your candor."

"Well, you see, Roy, I know how important this Cost Project is to you and Saco-Lowell and I know you're concerned about the quality of our work. So I think it's important to keep you informed. I know I may have seemed a little distant in my conversations around the other guys. Since they don't know me too well anyway, I'm not too worried about what they think. But I care what *you* think!"

"I've surveyed your work; and as you know, I've met with the two guys on the Roll Job and all seems to be OK. But quite apart from those connections, Joe, how are *you* doing? Any progress with the marital situation?"

Joe remained silent, started to tear up, clearly feeling sorry for himself, wiped his eyes, then went on at great length about a phone call he'd had with his wife. She'd been contacted by the

Saco police fishing for clues. Luckily they seem not to have told her the whole story, but enough to make her more curious than ever. "Naturally," he explained, "she called me every rotten name that rumbled through her mind, and I didn't help any by firing back. She has a lawyer, swears that she'll strip me of every penny before she's through. Now I know what friends have meant when they observed that there's no such thing as a 'friendly divorce.' But I didn't reveal any details about that girl's being ravaged. Oh, I forgot to tell you that Pete and I had an interchange and I denied knowing anything more about it. He didn't push me so I didn't lose my poise."

"So what may happen next?" I inquired.

"I don't know and that's what worries me just a bit."

"Do you think you'll be able to stick it out on this job? You surely realize our time constraints!"

"Yeah, and I'll stay no matter what she does. In fact, I'm in the process of getting a NYC lawyer who will insure my staying; it's only a couple more months, at most, before I planned to return, that is, when our Cost Job is finished."

"I appreciate that, Joe. Anything more that I can do?"

"At the moment, I don't think so. You've been most understanding and I thank you for that, Roy."

"Well, it's the least I could do. I've always said that everybody has a story to tell if there's anybody to listen."

"I agree and I'll keep you posted. And I've still not told anybody else about this even though my two friends at the Roll Job, Mannie and Art, have hinted and asked, 'Is there something wrong?' Probably it's because I occasionally come late and they've boasted about their workers never being tardy."

"Well, Joe, you could always tell them that I needed to talk with you, and that would be the truth. They don't need to know what topics we're discussing."

"I'd thought of saying that, but it helps to hear you suggest it. I think they're sensitive about the fact that we engineers are earning much higher salaries than they because they've mentioned that, too."

I chuckled a little at that comment because I'd heard it from other shop foreman, always skeptical of "outsiders" and other high-paid members of Saco-Lowell's management. Two inevitable products: "envy" and "sweat equity."

"OK, Joe, thanks for the confidence. Let's get back to work." He headed for the shops and I to the nearby office.

Once back, Grace reported that Harry Sawyer had called. "The Ordinance men, some in full military uniform are here and they'll be ready for you in fifteen minutes . . . just about time for you to reach Terminations."

When I reached the second floor of the old Pepperell Building across Pearl Street and the railroad tracks from the Pepperell cotton storehouse, the auditors were just sitting down. I walked in, recognized "the tall dark and handsome Army Captain," shook hands coolly, "Glad to see you!" [even if I wasn't!] I shook the others' hands while walking around the perimeter of the table, finally shook Harry's hand after all of his introductions. Ostensibly I was there simply to support Harry's contentions about the value of the so-called "lost casting." During an early-morning session they'd already come to an agreement about the miscellaneous items which we'd had to sort out as "surplus" some months before. In fact I'd helped with that just before assuming responsibility for the Cost Project.

Harry opened the discussion by pointing to the now Spic-and-Span cleaned, forged steel casting lying just outside the conference arena. He then outlined the various steps wherein Ford had ordered so many bogey wheels, how they'd cut back their order, how our tool design engineers had ordered enough

125

of these rough castings for the order. But then Ford's purchasing department reduced the order, making this particular casting superfluous. Harry was meticulous in his analysis, had a flow chart for the order, its delivery, its being missed and then discovered, and so on . . .

During his analysis, I studied the faces of the auditors. Rarely had I seen a group of men more bored and seemingly indifferent. While they talked I was so struck by the tone of the meeting I even scribbled a short dialogue between the Casting and the Chief Auditor:

Casting: Of course I went on a trip.

Auditor: Shut up, you're worthless!

Casting: I expected to have a distinguished career here at Saco-Lowell.

Auditor. I said you should shut up!

Casting: But I'm a good person.

Auditor: It doesn't matter. I said, *You're worthless.*

I also studied Harry's face. He was as nervous as the proverbial witch and I'm asking myself, "Do I want to remain at Saco-Lowell and stay involved in such pettiness when some of our arrogant military 'bureaucrazies' waste more money per hour than this equipment is worth? And what about the auditors, as I glanced around the table guessing how much tax money was being spent per minute . . . and I caught myself in a cost analysis mode, wondering what in hell difference did it make? Would a PhD from Harvard be worth all of that money either?"

I must have been in a trance because I finally heard Harry call my name. I was worse than the schoolboy who couldn't answer a teacher's simple question.

After a pause that seemed like an eternity, I said, "Harry, I was just speculating about what the lost casting may have cost us in the way of our time, looking for it and whether or not that cost should be added? Also, did we ever discover who buried it?"

This stimulated the chief auditor to speak quite sharply and loudly to ask, "Did you say it had been *lost*?"

I looked at Harry who gave me a look that would kill! But he recovered long enough to observe, "Sir, I . . . "

He was cut off by the army officer, "It's Captain, sir!"

Harry retorted, "Sorry sir, I mean 'Captain,' I'm not used to military protocol!"

I wasn't sure whether Harry wanted to kill me more than I'd have liked to kill the army officer so speaking firmly, "I think that this is ridiculous. Let's get back to the paper work. The castings, which we had manufactured outside this company because we didn't have the facilities to make them, cost us $527.94 each. We know what it cost for the five that we milled in our own machine shop. We know the cost of each operation done here. We are dickering over the one cut by Milling Machine #2748, a cut that was clearly finished. Only one operation got messed up by the unfortunate fact that the casting was buried by somebody and none of us know who did it. So it seems to me that we have a fairly clear idea as to the cost of this one ugly casting which missed its calling to be identified and bought by the US Army after we in good conscience should be able to make a quick decision. I for one do not like this petty bickering any more than I did the last time we met, *Sir!*"

I looked across the table as I said, "*Sir,*" flagrantly departing from military protocol.

Obviously the Army captain was angry, but at that point Harry spoke up to save the captain's face. He remarked. "I agree that Roy has all the facts straight even if I don't agree with his tone of voice."

There was a long pause and several persons took long deep breaths almost simultaneously.

Finally Harry spoke up, "I propose that we forget the history of this casting while in-house here at Saco-Lowell. The casting exists. I propose that the U.S. Army pay Saco-Lowell the $527.94 which it cost us to have it made outside the shops; here's the invoice; there's the casting. Take it away."

But the captain, obviously used to lording it over his underlings would not let go, observing, "I resent Mr. Fairfield's commentary as well as the implications that the U.S. Treasury is a bottomless pit of money. Is there no patriotism at this table?"

This made me even angrier and I looked desperately at Harry. He shook his head side to side and quietly put his finger across his mouth. He then spoke up saying in a very low voice. "I don't think this has anything to do with patriotism and I resent the implications of your remark, Captain."

A seeming eternity passed and nothing was said for several minutes as the atmosphere cooled down. Finally Harry spoke again. "Sir . . . I mean Captain, I know that Ford Motor Company, with military support, cut the size of the order. Let's adjourn."

19. TIME-CLOCK CULTURE

It may speak too generally or anthropologically to call Saco Lowell a "time-clock culture." Yet, it's amazing how powerful the clock is when determining how employees and managers set goals and evaluate production (note that the Cost Project's very objectives were time-based). For instance, time for each operation related to employees' wages, mechanisms on machines, skill in utilizing those machines and so on ad infinitum. While a Bedaux process-observer might use a stop-watch, employees were paid on the basis of "punching in" on the time clock when they entered their particular department or worked on a specific job.

History of the abuse of the clock runs in many directions. Some factory owners in the early industrial era were notoriously "criminal" in setting clocks back five to ten minutes after work began in order to get that much more work out of their employees' flesh and do it wholesale. After all, five or ten minutes times 100, 500, or 1000 employees added up to that much more production, hence increasing profit for the owner, corporate stock holders and so on. Naturally, with so many employees serving as watchdogs, the clock-tinkerers couldn't always get away with such clock readjusting. Hence, this was an issue for the early unions.

Another practice which I watched rather closely among office workers at the shops; namely, employees leaving their desks as much as five to ten minutes early, lining up at the clock in order to get just under the wire, thereby avoiding any tendency to give the shops any extra minutes any time of day. If by any chance or design the clock did not work correctly, somebody would immediately notify whoever was in charge so that Payroll would assume that everybody left at their appointed hour; in most cases, unless under special rules such as the Cost Project, the office check-in times were eight and one, the check-out times at twelve and five o'clock. It varied in the shops. Being paid time and a half was a function of both scheduled and permitted "overtime," for holidays, nights and special assignments. Although managers and foremen might have fixed salaries, they were expected to punch in when they came and went. In my own case when on regular assignment in the early years working there, I became known as a so-called "eager beaver." I never calculated how many hours I worked for nothing; my accomplishments seemed to be noticed and my job description, assignment and salary changed accordingly.

One could discuss at length the way in which Saco-Lowell practiced American customs via celebration of national holidays and local customs. The Shops usually joined the patriotic flow with floats in the local parades, raised and lowered the flags, at half and full mast, depending upon the customs. Those with roots in Quebec sometimes returned to Canada to start gardens; in fact, sometimes the Shops, as well as the local textile mills, shut down completely a couple of summer weeks so as to keep production flowing smoothly and not subject the two communities to a jerky stop-and-start routine.

Individuals observed Maine's autumn hunting season whether industry's wheels kept turning or not. Social life, via sports teams, local clubs, etc. also fit the pattern of other segments of local society. Consistent with the theme of a clock-watching society, each of these activities were timely; likewise fund-raising for "good causes" such as United Way and organizations such as Rotary and the Chamber of Commerce. One might easily extrapolate Saco-Lowell's reflection of local culture and vice versa. The demography of the two cities also tended to reflect employees in two major divisions: the more skilled and highly educated workers tended to live in Saco whereas their opposites tended to be Biddeford residents . . . although as the years passed both groups tended to spread across both cities.

When it came to the "work ethic," it is fair to observe that the nature of production demanded hard-working, highly-skilled employees. In one sense, as in many other segments of American society, the time clock was a symbol of efficiency and progress especially when the Shops felt the heat of the so-called Great Depression and the competition with other textile machine manufacturers, such as Whitin Machine Works of Whitinsville, Massachusetts.

One negative footnote: while it was clear to me from the first day I set foot in Saco-Lowell Shops, June 24, 1936, that the clock-watching culture was based upon a fundamental distrust of human nature in an increasingly technological society, I also noted that things would probably be chaotic if each employee were to set her or his own standards for attendance and/or tending and respecting the workplace. Likewise, if the clock-watching at every level of machine manufacturing were not coordinated with use of the clock, chaos might reign. Also, it's a function of magnitude; but, for better or worse, it relates to a computer-driven society. Nor can one forget the checks and balances that are woven into the spirit and mechanism of American government at local, state and national levels. Not all of these factors were in play in 1944, but it was not difficult to extrapolate the trends.

131

20. ACCULTURATION/ALIENATION

There's an old and somewhat crude saying that "you can't call yourself a 'Maineac' until you can pee on your grandfather's grave!" However true or imaginative that expression may be, it had utility in such situations as mine, trying to bring the Cost Project to successful completion with engineers "from away," another expression which sometimes bothers me during my fairly long life.

My use of such a gross phrase came early in the life of the project when some of the engineers began to comment upon Mainers' speech patterns. By using such terms as "Ay-ah" and the classical test question, "Have ya pahkt ya cahr in the gahrahg'?" I chuckled both with and at them when the question arose. Some of the men had been in Maine before, hence they tried to put these expressions into context. I described myself as a "Maineac" since my grandfather was buried locally. Also I differentiated between "Maineac" and "Mainer," the latter expression used to describe a person who had recently adopted the state as "home." It was all in good banter and none of the persons seemed to be truly demeaning in discussing it.

In recent years, when comparing the Saco-Lowell situation with that at Bates College in 1947, when bus loads of out-of-state male students fanned throughout Maine fighting forest fires, then returned to Lewiston and yelled to one another across the campus landscapes literally mocking the Maineacs they had encountered in various local communities, there was a major difference. The mechanical engineers were much more cosmopolitan; they had worked at various jobs around the United States and seemed to have encountered different ethnic groups, hence were probably more tolerant than the Bates fellows (women made sandwiches for the fire fighters, didn't work on fire fronts).

I encountered a different brand of criticism when one of the engineers, a man who had spent several years of his life in France, asked if anybody had listened to the local radio station. He observed that the announcers and Biddeford residents "mangled" the French language. They merely modified technical terms by fracturing some words and pasted pieces of French and English together. He did not criticize the "mangling" with a mean demeanor. Rather, he said he was "puzzled." I then told him the story of an argument that I'd had with one of my assistants in the Terminations Program. She insisted that the way to pronounce "potato" was "potaht." I was quite defensive in arguing that "No! It's 'pom de terre,' or 'apple of the ground.'" She was equally insistent with her "potaht" version of the French word, urged me to listen to the radio and I would "hear it the correct way." I countered by bringing to the office a copy of a French Dictionary. I showed it to her, but she didn't believe it. That running interchange lasted until I left the Terminations Department to go to the University of Colorado to learn Japanese in a U.S. Naval program.

The engineers' discussion of the cultural variations was a lesson for all of us, an opportunity to discuss ethnic variations although our main task was cost analysis. Although we later ran into the anti-Semitism already discussed earlier (Chapter 3), it did afford me the opportunity to dip into a variety of ethnic issues that became an important factor in my ability to talk with them both in and out of the office. Also, it expanded my own horizons which, before college, were incredibly naïve and parochial.

A more exciting and constructive aspect of my interaction with the engineers happened when they sought suggestions of "places to go" and "things to see." Sometime I felt more like a member of the local Chamber of Commerce or the Maine Tourist Bureau than the coordinator of the Saco-Lowell Cost Analysis Project! But anyway . . .

Early in the program and especially for those who had never been in Maine, some wanted to know about beaches, so I told them about Old Orchard, Long Beach in York; others wanted to know specifically about Fortunes Rocks and Crescent beaches. Some inquired about museums so I paid high praise to the York Institute (now Saco Museum) and the Bowdoin Art Museum. A few of the more hardy souls asked the way to Mt. Washington, Katahdin, Cadillac Mountain and the Appalachian Trail, and I added Douglas Hill. As for Maine lobster and clams: I needed not point too far. I thought of attempting to organize a clambake, in the mode in which Maryllyn's family created them, but decided it was too much work and probably would be perceived as a "conflict of interest." But I did organize a local history tour, by foot on Main Streets in both Saco and Biddeford, as well as by car, ranging between Cascades and Cataract Falls as well as the historic section of Kennebunkport's colonial houses.

Later in the season, when some of the men brought their families to Maine for one and two-week vacations, I sometimes met them for shop lunch or dinner in town so that they could extract information from me quickly and save time to get their vacation under way without a lot of research. I also showed them the way to some of our less publicized recreation places, such as East Sebago State Park, Kennebunk Pond and Mousam Lake. Most people preferred beach resorts to lakes and ponds. But at any rate and in spite of my reservations about tourism, I felt that it was more in the spirit of friendliness to do this extracurricular advising in my nonworking hours.

In the same spirit with which I had accepted an invitation to dinner by George Lincoln Spielman, I accepted an invitation for Maryllyn and me to have dinner with Fritz Zimmerman, especially after his encounter with John MacScott who was either upset by Fritz's being Jewish or too slow with his work . . . or both. The evening was a success for me, but once we repaired to his Saco Main Street rented room after dinner, it was a disaster for Maryllyn.

Fritz was rather slow of speech and a meticulous person, very proud of his invention of a power plane with which to plane the surfaces of ocean-going ship propellers. As anybody might surmise, the machine to do that job was gigantic, filled with all manner of stop mechanisms and motions, cams and cogs by the bushel. Although Fritz knew that I was no engineer, he insisted upon discussing the most minute details, encouraging me to follow the manual from his patent papers with attached diagrams. I followed him fairly well as long as he stuck to the diagrams, but he lost me when he got into the mathematics and how he circumvented various planes and problems via calculus. In short, I got the "major drift" and Fritz backed off or up a few times when I said, "I don't understand."

Meanwhile, Maryllyn had brought nothing to read and Fritz had no general reading materials in his room, so she pretended to listen but was bored to tears. At a crucial moment when Fritz paused, she reminded me that we had an errand to do for our daughter and must attend to that while the stores were open and before returning to our rented room. Fritz seemed to be a little bothered by our abrupt leaving, but I suggested that he bring his patent and diagrams to work someday if he were "kind enough to finish explanations" some noon at lunch. He was very pleasant, thanked us both and we reciprocated for "dinner and insights pertaining to his fantastic invention." He did bring in the papers and we had a noon session one noon after lunch and my routine encounter with *The Magic Mountain* . . . but a surprise one at that!

21. COURTESY VISITS

At the end of August Grace reminded me that for human relations' sake I'd better visit Spindles, Comber and Slasher Departments. Their foremen had been cooperative and the data the
engineers had obtained was seemingly complete and clear. I had
double-checked with the engineers we assigned to their departments, but Grace shook her head knowingly, concluding, "One
never knows!" I asked her to be candid, but all she would say
was, "I have a feeling!"

I charged it off to intuition, but continued, "OK, see if you
can get me appointments with the three foremen, one this afternoon with John Green at Spindles and the other two guys
tomorrow or next day."

I went back to the conference room for a quiet space carry-
ing a stack of cost reports, attempting to clear cost discrepancies
which Grace and Priscilla were unable to fathom. It was a
tedious job matching specific operations with particular
machines. With all our joint office efforts, we still had only two
machines completely accounted for except for overhead on key
Foundry items. I made another, the humpty-ninth note to
myself: *Get after Kettley to provide the overhead percentages*. In fact,
I phoned Lawrence Perry, Kettley's secretary, to see if there had
been a breakthrough. There were no new developments, so I
encouraged him to mention it as an Undone Task. Lawrence

stammered a bit, a characteristic gesture when he knew he was against a stone wall!

Grace knocked gently, came in and announced, "Fritz would like to see you. Shall I send him in?" I must have grimaced and hesitated because she asked, "O.K.?"

I replied "O.K." "Did you get John Green at Spindles?"

"Fine, right after lunch!"

A few seconds later Fritz shuffled through the Conference Room door. I welcomed him with, "We enjoyed dinner and the propeller lecture the other night."

Fritz, always affable, observed, "Pretty technical?"

"Yes," I replied, "but think I got the major drift, especially the implications for producing Liberty Ships and future ship-building for ocean-going liners."

"Good, when shall I finish the lecture?"

I fibbed a little. "Can't do it today because I've got a date with Spindles and tomorrow or next day with Slashers and Combers. How about two or three days after tomorrow, at noon?"

Fritz smiled and left both quickly and silently, a really nice old guy. I made a note of the conversation and appointment, then continued with pursuit of the correct machines and match with cost sheets so Grace and Priscilla could finish them. When the noon whistle blew, I fetched my box lunch and *The Magic Mountain*. Also I began to curse my compulsive behavior; once I start a book, I seem to be compelled to finish it as well as write reactions to it. I mused about that as I thought of my old Bates 'prof' and mentor who "preached habit and follow-through." One of his many pieces of advice: "If you have something to do, do it immediately and you only have to do it once!" With that thought, I dived back into Thomas Mann until I began hearing the multiple "Ding-Dings" of the distant time clocks! So much for the dilemma of Hans Catsorp in his sanatorium on the magic mountain, feeling that I *must finish the book before leaving S-L-S!* Yet, with Fritz's poignant story in prospect, I had a new incentive to do just that!

Checked in briefly with Grace as I handed her the completed stack of cost sheets, ready for her Frieden calculator, then dashed off to see John Green at Spindles. John, a tall, raw-boned, rugged Maine native welcomed me in his usual glad-handed way. His second-hand, Jim Gillespie, came in, somewhat breathless, to report a worker having passed out on a machine and the fact that he'd sent Joe Cote to the infirmary with a fellow worker who operated a nearby machine, "Same symptoms as last time, John, he seems asthmatic; perhaps we should insist that Joe see a local doctor?"

"O.K. with me," John responded. "Maybe we've been too slow in recommending that. Go ahead, take whatever action that's needed." He then turned to me to ask, "Reason for your visit, Roy?"

"John, I've not avoided you. Rather our outside engineer, Mike Stern, has insured me that things are going well here, so I didn't want to interfere in any way. But I wish I were a little clearer about the ring assemblies as I check their costs. I know that we machine the ring rails and some of the spindle assemblies, but where does the outside vendor enter the pictures? You've got all kinds of examples here in your office. Also, maybe you could clarify the processes for me. Incidentally, congratulations for your new patents and the National Award from the World Spindle Association. Publicity for Saco-Lowell is always good to see; to counter some of the negative PR that we get from the local media when our smokestacks smoke or our riverside trash pollutes its banks. We all know that syndrome!"

"Yeah," said John as he stepped to the subassembly on the

office display bench. "It was good to be recognized. I even got a congratulatory note from the Admiral who conducted the Navy's 'E–Day Award for Excellence' last winter."

"I hope the corporate officers have been equally generous."

"Can't complain," John said, quietly.

"Maybe only scuttlebutt; please don't quote me, but I suspect we'll see all kinds of frosting even though we don't taste much cake!"

John chuckled at the metaphor, but proceeded to lead me through the various phases of the operation of the spindle, how the thread came between the top and bottom rolls, passed through the ring assembly to give the thread an extra twist before winding up on the spindle and thus making it stronger for use in the looms. I asked several questions pertaining to that phase of the operation, also when, how and when his breakthrough occurred and what made it more advanced than the previous design.

He then led me through the way changes in materials and varying speeds had made its improvement possible. I didn't understand the mathematics any more than I did when Fritz Zimmerman used similar calculations to "prove" the practicality of his ocean propeller plane. But with Jim Gillespie at his side, John was very painstaking in his explanations, which lasted for fifteen or twenty minutes. He then had Jim take me into the machine area of the Spindle Department to give me a first-hand sense of the difference between old and new methods of machining and polishing.

I couldn't have asked for clearer explanations to enable me to interpret the cost sheets which our outside engineer, Mike Stern, turned in as his part in the Cost analysis.

Thanking John and Jim profusely, I started to leave when Superintendent Jim Crosby came through the door, greeted me pleasantly and jokingly asked, "Did John share all his secrets with you?"

I laughed and retorted, "He had a difficult student. Remember, I was a Humanities major, English, in college!"

"Yeah," retorted Crosby, "but you got your education here long before you went to Bates!"

"True, but I'm still not much good at math!"

"That's OK, Roy, so long as you deliver the cost job for Black and Kettley, we'll never fault you!"

"Thank you, sir, I appreciate your confidence."

"Ever since I witnessed one and heard the tales of your handling the other foreman for their anti-Semitism, names we'll not mention" (and he stole a glance at John Green and Jim Gillespie as he spoke), "you'll do OK as a member of our team." Glanced at John and he merely shrugged.

I thought it time to leave lest another embarrassment might arise, shook hands all around and headed for the erecting floor and the Ford bogey wheel assembly line. I thought it was time for a quick hello to Uncle Frank and dad; and, luckily I caught them both on their 15-minute rest period as they were together. Dad had just told Uncle Frank one of his garage stories and they were both laughing uproariously. They didn't stop even when they spied me turning off from one of the long corridors and just missed being hit by one of the little shop tractors towing a trailer filled with bogey wheel castings.

They both greeted me warmly and shook hands to share some of the cast iron dust or grease in which they "bathed" freely.

"What's the joke?" I asked.

"I'll tell you later," dad remarked, and Uncle Frank observed, "You're too young to hear it!"

"Oh, one of those?" I inquired, but not really wanting to trade stories but learn from each, "How ya doing?"

Uncle Frank, nodding toward the machine on which he'd been working for a couple of months, observed, "the old 'hoss' is still there, waiting to be fully broken in!" I laughed at his metaphor and asked somewhat sarcastically, "What's the matter with the Red Sox. Looks as though they couldn't beat the Old Men's Home team!"

"Not a good year to follow them; maybe we can get to Fenway next summer to help them improve their record!?"

Dad spoke up, "You know, Roy, thanks to you and your training your mother to listen to Sox games on the radio, she 'attends' every game from Fenway Park, cheers at their hits, boos at their errors."

"Not too different from when I was at Thornton; but how's the Ford inspection job going, dad?"

"Easier than it was. I've learned how to use leverage in wrestling with those huge castings. And the tool designers have created a jig, kind of a saddle-like tool hooked to the ceiling with a strong cord, on which the castings ride up the assembly line. So the new system means I don't have to juggle them physically, simply apply the 'Go' and 'No-Go' gauges. If they don't pass the test, however, I have to lift them off the line and set them aside for re-machining. Not many in that category . . . so it's much easier than it used to be when I moved from those damnable 'razor-back' Sylvania fuse-cans to Ford. I thought for sure I was 'gonna' cut off a finger before I mastered the technique for handling them."

"In short, dad, you're happier today than when you first started war work?"

"Yeah, and I feel a twinge of patriotism now and then when I see the three flags flying over this building. I know we're doing what we can to help the boys overseas."

I didn't share my reservations about Saco-Lowell's contri-

142

butions, but there was no point in doing that as long as he felt wanted and was contributing to the war work. He'd just missed the draft in WWI. Simply by being born in 1918, I may have helped keep him alive? Who would ever know?

I crossed him off my mental worry list, bid good-bye to both him and Uncle Frank and started back to the office. I'd not gone far when another transportation tractor driver nearly ran me over. I just barely stepped out of the aisle before he roared along, saw me step into a "puddle" of oil, and I heard him laughing hilariously as he rolled along thru the erecting-room corridor. This had happened to me several times when I first joined Saco-Lowell as a green kid and even more recently. My friend, Ralph Perry had advised me not to make a big thing about it. These drivers in the Transportation Department had the reputation of being "thugs" and had been known to injure others, especially those who worked in the offices but had to go into the shops to do their jobs. Johnny Morin, Foreman of Transportation had once been discovered to have put out what they called a "contract" on a member of the Purchasing Department, but it became a "public secret" and both Morin and his driver were suspended for a month each as a first warning; one more evidence of any crime-like behavior of this kind and they both would be fired.

Hence, as I detoured around the most open places in the Yard, I wondered if I, a fairly well-known office worker, had stumbled into another pending "contract!" As I kept on my course toward my office, I could see through the little booth at the intersection of the Saco-Biddeford covered bridge and the main drag along the scrap iron piles with their overhead whinnying cranes, and saw that Johnny, the Transportation Foreman, was at his desk. So I decided to pay him a brief visit to complain of my near-accident. I knew that he knew me, so I put my head into his office door to ask, "Hi, Johnny, busy?"

143

"'Shu-ah,' always am, what can I do for 'ya'?"

I told him about times and places of my near accidents, especially the one with a guy roaring down the Erection Room floor. I concluded with the question, "Is there a contract out on my hide?"

He laughed, became defensive, grumped, "Of course not! And I'm asking, "Are you accusing me of having you run over?"

"No! I'm just hoping that your driver isn't doing somebody else's bidding!"

"Can you describe the tractor driver?"

"Yes!" . . . and I did the best I could to tell his boss how he appeared to me, "rather burly, with a somewhat worried face and a Red Sox cap firmly pulled down on his head."

"Oh, that's probably Charlie Mack, he sometimes drives a little recklessly."

"Well, he'd better not try it again!!" I threatened. "One scandal of its kind is too many for a place like these shops!" I turned without further comment, stepped down and out from his strategically located office, looked back to see him turn to speak with his secretary-clerk. I couldn't hear what he said, but he was clearly angry. I beat a hasty retreat, feeling that I may have overstepped my bounds when feeling so outraged!

Grace and Priscilla noted my anger and sweat-saturated shirt and asked in unison, "Is anything wrong?"

"Yes, but there's probably nothing we can do about it. Almost got run over near the Biddeford Erecting Floor."

Both women looked back to their work desks.

Settling at my desk, I scribbled a couple of items:

. . . a word with Charlie, the Yank;

. . . visit to Slasher and Comber departments

. . . in two days—visit with Fritz Zimmerman to finish the propeller planing lecture.

22. OF SLASHING & COMBING

After opening the office that Tuesday morning, I spent an hour tying up odds and ends, "passing the time of day" with a few of the engineers, confirmed Wednesday's noon appointment with Fritz Zimmerman, checked both Grace and Priscilla for progress and needs for more cost sheets. Also had a conference with Charlie Crogan, who by now was known as "The Yank!" Either he or the engineer on the Screw Machine Job scrambled some of the figures, hence he could not derive the cost for each part as they came off the machine. In short, it was a routine day opener. It was also muggy and some of the early ground fog hung in the canyons between our building and the Pepperell loom sheds beyond the rooftops. As I left the office group, Grace and Priscilla, almost in unison warned, "Keep your cool."

"Fat chance!" I retorted and headed for my visits with Joe Kelly in Slashers and Sven Olsen in Combers, departments which made machines to size yarn and comb long-staple cotton.

Although it was blistering hot walking across the yard and circumnavigating the slag heaps before waving casually to Johnny Morin in the Transportation Office and crossing the River to the Saco side, I rode to the top story via the rickety old freight elevator. Actually, there wasn't much happening at Kelly's Slasher operation. The Shops were building one standard machine with the prospect of having an order shortly after the war ended. One worker was bending four-foot copper sheets near one end of the department; and watching him along with Kelly, I was reminded of my first visit there in 1936 when I was running around the shops a couple of times a day revising Specification and Lists of parts to reflect various mills' changes in their orders. Close to Kelly's ear, I whispered above the general noise level in the building, "You know, Kelly, the first time I was ever here, not long after graduating from Thornton Academy, I was very impressed by your men's adroit handling of those large sheets of copper and your testing of the sizing pots. I'd seen copper tubing and small pieces of roof flashing before, but never the sheets that went into those huge copper slasher drums."

He replied in his delightful Irish brogue, "Yeah, in the days before the war, those sheets might be a much as ten to fifteen feet long, probably forty or so inches wide. Then demand from various military establishments took that stuff off the market so we've had to stick smaller pieces together with whatever materials we could find . . . chewing gum or tobacco juice if necessary," and he grinned while snapping his eyes open and closed!

"I might have wondered about that, but didn't know about it," I said. "And did this create any problems when it came to balancing cylinders on your whirly-gig machines?"

"Did it ever! When we added all of those welding materials to the surfaces of the cylinders, we created all kinds of wobbles. Because the surfaces touching the yarn required such close tolerances, it probably took us three to five times as long to do the balancing as during the so-called 'good old days.'"

"I appreciate your going over all of this with Fritz Zimmerman during his short stay with you when he was visiting around. Was sorry that slashers were not included among the representative machines we're costing out. I suspect that Kettley may simply go to Purchasing to find out how much the price of copper has skyrocketed since the war began. I'll bet it's more than the five-to-ten percent that he estimates other materials have risen in price."

"I don't know for sure, Roy, because it's been more or less irrelevant since we've not had many orders recently. Wouldn't surprise me if it had climbed more than 100%."

He paused, looked around in both directions as though to check the security of his environment, then in a low whisper asked, "How's Fritz Zimmerman doing down with MacScott? I hear that they had a confrontation?"

"Well, Kelly," I responded cautiously, not wanting to get entangled in shop politics, "I don't know what the scuttlebutt is, but they had a few words and reached an agreement."

"Good, I like Mac even though his background is Scottish and mine is Irish. We've divorced our ancestors! We talk bluntly about them. I liked Fritz, too, even though I found him a bit slow on the draw."

I chuckled a little and added, "That seemed to be MacScott's view too. But, we can't all be speed demons."

"That would never describe Fritz," Kelly said as he walked me toward the elevator. I thanked him for his time, indicated that I was leaving the Shops in October. "Might not see you again before I leave." As I stepped onto the elevator, he said, "Good luck on your doctorate. Come back to see us some school vacation." Little did I imagine that dad would become one of his workers after the War.

Getting off the rickety old elevator in the Small Machines Department, I could not but notice the character of that long narrow room, where once York Manufacturing Company once ran its textile machines and the aisles were full of noisy, whipping belts that ran off the overhead countershafts and the smaller machines (punch presses, drill presses, engine lathes, the fundamental tools for making tools and parts). Whereas the flapping belts *once* endangered all employees but especially ME as I was forced to walk between the machines from the stairwells to the foreman's office, *now* each machine had its own motor. It was a welcome change and I mentioned it to Department Foreman, Sven Olsen; as I walked in and shook his hand.

He smiled in acknowledging my observation. "You know, Roy, I remember your telling me about your fears when you were runner boy, coming twice a day to update our documents. Oh! Yes! And your horrible dreams!"

"That was more than eight years ago, but I remember it as though it were yesterday. In fact I'm not sure that I ever thanked you enough for showing me the way from stairwells to the office to avoid the flying belts. I think you empathized with me because one of your apprentice machinists had lost an arm a few months before I came to the shops to work."

"Your memory is both vivid and accurate," Sven confirmed. "Now, what can I do for you today?"

"Sven, may I call you by your first name . . . ?"

"Of course, of course, we're all in this together!"

"First I want to inquire if you're still satisfied with Norm Cohn, and do he and Ernie Trachtberg take up a lot of your time? As we discussed the matter over the phone, you make such a variety of parts here, especially in tooling up the combers, I felt it imperative to place two engineers in your department so as to even-out costing production."

Sven responded quickly, "Once we found space for them to work and located a master list of our machine tools, they seemed to do OK . . . and as a team they get along with most of our men although some of our women at the drill presses disturb them; I could be wrong but all of our men would probably feel more comfortable if our female crew all wore overalls and didn't have such shapely bodies! Or at least they tell me they're pretty."

I chuckled and said, "Come on, Sven, you know that old saw about a woman's being as old as she looks, but a guy's old when he stops looking!"

"Apt observation," Swen nodded, "but most of the guys' stories and observations are not as clean as that. Actually, I have to command '*Out of bounds*' loudly when some of the guys start telling stories that turn some of the women's faces red, and I'm not kidding. But, look, Roy, you didn't come over to discuss shop morals, or did you?"

I laughed and said, "Of course not, but I suppose these issues are as much facts of shop life as boring a 2.56" hole in a carrier arm on one of those combers" and I nodded toward a fully-erected experimental machine.

"Yer right, but I sometimes take shop mores for granted and absorb them automatically while my second-hands remind me that 'It ain't so!' But anyway . . . "

Then he continued, "I like both Norm and Ernie. As both engineers and persons they're both very competent. They are sticking close to your Cost Project objectives, and minding their own business. While I know that we're writing history, I sometimes have gone to them with a particular engineering problem related to the experiments we're doing (even with the war on) to improve the operation of the post-war comber."

"Fascinating," I observed, "would you mind showing me what you're doing?"

"Come on over here," he beckoned as he walked toward the full-sized comber erected toward the end of the machining room. "As you well know, Roy, this is a very complicated machine. While it's designed to comb long fibers of what is euphemistically called 'Sea Island Cotton,' not all fibers fit the specifications, hence we have to allow for variations in that fiber. To me this is a continuously experimental machine. I sometimes wonder how we've managed to place so many highly regarded machines out there in production in those mills."

He turned on the power to a segment of the machine set up to run independently of the other parts of the frame. Although long ago I'd had a demonstration of a comber to help me understand its working parts and their names, I'd not remembered many of the details.

Once the machine was up to speed and the combing arms were combing the sliver or skein of fiber in rhythmic strokes, as though being done by hand, he pointed to the way in which the cotton was doubling in such a way as to skip those fibers that sort of hung off in mid-air. Sven then said, "There's our problem. You might say that some of the fibers being uneven, and getting cotton to grow perfectly evenly or with all fibers being of the same length, is practically impossible despite all the experimenting there's been over the decades. So, as Ernie Trachtberg astutely observed the other day: 'You need to control the body of cotton on these machines much as you do the others, but how to do it with the comber arms occupying the spaces where the controls might be?'"

I didn't quite understand *all* of Sven's lingo, but I kept looking and listening. Sven must have read my puzzled expression; after he shut down the machine, he beckoned me to follow him to the office where he dug out some sketches marked, "E.T." for the visiting engineer's initials. Sven then said, "A day or two after I showed the problem to Ernie, he asked to see the prints for the gear trains, took some of them home, then came in with these sketches which he said he'd made the previous night. I proceeded to show them to our engineers over in Research and

Development. And they're in the process of incorporating a new design into the comber arm as well as modify the gear train with more cams."

"Amazing!" I exclaimed. "And is Ernie happy about this outcome?"

"I surmise he is because our R & D is contemplating hiring him when your Cost Project is completed."

"And all this going under my very nose!" I mused.

"Not really, Roy. It's happened outside shops time up to this very minute. We were careful about that; and, except for first demonstrating the problem to Ernie here on our machine, we've done it at dinner at my home on two separate evenings. We all heard about the flap between Al and Spielman over on the Gear Job and with Mac and Fritz down in Sheet Metal so we didn't want to repeat those awkward events; and you know how closed-mouth R&D is about developmental progress and process. Too, Kettley and Crosby made it clear that the imported engineers were to write history and not recommend new designs. Yes, you may have been by-passed, Roy, up to now, but Kettley knows about it. I don't know if Black does."

I reacted quietly, "Sven, I'm truly amazed and pleased. I had contemplated a meeting toward the end of the Cost Project, if it happened before I left for Cambridge, a meeting at which we gathered both the engineers and our R&D folk to ask for specific suggestions because it seemed almost irresponsible to bring so much high-paid talent to Saco-Lowell, then *not* take full advantage of it . . . in fact it seemed that such a meeting, with specific follow-up would pay handsome dividends in the postwar period. "

"Did you suggest that to Black or Kettley?"

"I hadn't gotten around to it because it seemed beyond my assignment and jurisdiction, nor did I want to mention it to the

engineers for fear that they would begin to forget their assignments and like the good scientists/technologists that they are
might spend too much time tinkering with the future and too little on the history. But, Sven, I'm glad to hear your story but suggest we keep it under cover until we wrap up the project."

"Sounds good to me and you don't sound very upset about
what's happened."

"Surprised, but not upset! Possibly it demonstrates a cardi-
nal principle of development or as the great Alfred North
Whitehead argued, 'If you can't solve a problem, change it.'"
My dad once demonstrated this, and he surely had never heard
of Whitehead! When I was about ten and couldn't drop an oil
pan past the tie-rods of an old Buick, he listened to my whining
about why I couldn't do it. He was rather sharp with me, almost
shouting 'Listen, Roy, if you can't take the pan off the car, take
the car off the oil pan.'"

"Good story!" Sven exclaimed.

So I left the Comber department with my head spinning as
I ran down the stairwell . . . stopped a couple of times to look
out over the old York Mills (now Bates Manufacturing . . . meandered through MacScott's Sheet Metal and Paint Departments
. . . waved to Woody Pierre and Fritz as I hurried through . . .
stopped in the covered bridge to watch the river flow, ever so
slowly as we experienced the low-water season . . . walked
swiftly past Transportation (Johnny Morin was not there) . . .
stopped for a moment to watch the overhead crane dump a load
of scrap iron on the platform over the furnaces . . . bounded past
the Snagging Room door where the dust and noise were as thick
as ever . . . glanced quickly over the time cards beside the clock
to see that all of the engineers were still on the job . . . passed
quickly through the Drafting Room with an occasional "Hi" to
those not bending over their drawing tables . . . saw Mark Black

dictating letters to Ethel . . . waved down a long corridor of filing cabinets at Ralph Perry who happened to look up, then . . . walked into the Cost Project office at 11:50 to ask Grace, "Anything new?"

"Same old, same old, but you did get an interesting postal card from your old Bates mentor, Bob Berkelman."

"What did he say?"

"He got your letter, said he'd write you a longer note if his time were shorter!"

"Sounds like Bob, still dabbling in paradox!"

Grace squinted her nose and wrinkled her forehead.

I responded, "It's the other side of one of his favorite expressions, you know, 'If I'd had more time I'd have written a shorter letter!'"

"'You'se guys' never cease to amaze me!" then she went off to lunch as I picked up my copy of *The Magic Mountain*, wondering if I'd ever get Hans Catsorp out of his Alps sanatorium!

23. TWO TIMES THREE

At noon following my Slasher and Comber Department visits, I felt somewhat beaten; so, while the office folk all went out for lunch I sat back in my office chair, basked in the sun pouring through the dusty windows, closed my eyes, munched away and only reflected upon Hans Catsorp's destiny in that sanatorium. I'd still not read the final chapters of Mann's book so didn't really know his fate. The catnap that ensued restored some of my energy and I awakened with a snap upon hearing Fritz's voice mumble something . . . I snapped to attention, blinked and asked, "What did you say, Fritz?"

Fritz chuckled. "Sorry to wake you, but I was just checking to see if our appointment is OK for tomorrow noon."

"Of course, Fritz, I'm interested in hearing the last part of your story." I didn't *tell* him that I'd be glad to get the obligation over because it hung over me like the proverbial sword! We shook hands and he shuffled off to MacScott-ville!

Grace and Priscilla led the others for the afternoon shift, and we all plunged into afternoon details. I intended to carry the most troublesome cost sheets into our conference room. Before I settled down, Grace asked if she could see me "in private?" When we got together, Grace plunged into a troublesome issue with the blunt comment , "I don't think Lennie's working out!"

And before I could ask, "Why not?" she continued. "She

doesn't seem to be paying attention. She clearly hasn't mastered the Frieden calculator because I've found some glaring errors. I tried to get her to review and renew her techniques, but she was very defensive, almost screamed, 'I know what I'm doing!' I think, Roy, that she's being pressured by Spielman; she seems not to know that he's married or does know and doesn't care. I accidentally caught them smooching between the experimental machines the other day. I don't think they saw me, but I don't like what's happening!"

"What do you think we should do?"

"I'm not sure! I know she's a friend of Priscilla's; they once worked together making blueprints in the Reproduction Department."

"Yeah, I know; is Priscilla's aware of the situation?"

"I don't know, but it occurred to me that we might speak to her together."

"When?"

"How about right now?"

"O.K. with me, my afternoon's seems fairly clear."

So Grace went out to fetch Priscilla. They came back together and I started the conversation, "We seem to have a problem."

"With Lennie?" she queried.

"Then you know?" I asked.

"Well, sorta . . . I had a hunch . . ."

"What are you seeing?" Grace asked.

Priscilla's viewpoint wasn't too different from Grace's because she too had seen Spielman pick Lennie up in his car, and had found some errors when reviewing her calculations on the cost sheets.

I pursued another aspect of her assignment. "Has her work been otherwise satisfactory in processing cost sheets at Reproduction or finding specific blueprints in the vault?"

Priscilla thought for a moment, then replied, "For the most part, only a couple of times have I had to help her find specific prints, but one of those was not her fault, simply she didn't look hard enough."

"Well, ladies, what do you think we should do? I'm reluctant to try to find more help we're so far into the program. I'm also a bit leery of getting into an 'affair' which she may be having 'off campus' as it were . . . unless we can question the wisdom of a situation that seems to be distracting her. Incidentally, where is she right now?"

"At her desk," both responded in unison.

"What do you suggest that we do?"

We looked at one another for a minute or two, then Priscilla suggested that the three of us talk with her; that would underline the seriousness of the situation as related to the total Cost Project.

Grace looked at us both, then nodded in agreement.

I spoke up to say, "Then, let's not let it fester any longer; let's have her in." Grace went after her.

When Lennie came through the door, her eyes and face were red; she seemed to have been crying. She had her handkerchief clasped tightly in her fingers. Her clothing seemed a bit disheveled. I served as spokesman and asked, "Is there something you'd like to share with us, you seem to have been crying."

"Not really, but" . . . and she stopped.

At that point, Priscilla picked up the discussion and was quite direct, "Look, Lennie, you and I have known one another for some time. We're not going to get very far in this meeting unless you come clean. Something's wrong! What is it? You looked upset all morning. What's happening?" Again, a long pause as she broke down three times as she began to talk. We honored her silence, quietly looked at one another, but said nothing for what seemed like an eternity, probably only three or four minutes. She finally wiped her eyes, composed herself, then began her story. Spielman had roughed her up and tried to force her to have sex with him in his car the night before. She also learned for the first time that he was already married . . . and though she was in the process of divorcing her husband for physical brutality and double-timing her, she said she thought this man, who was highly educated and "seemed to be a nice guy" was honest. But, indeed, he wasn't.

We all listened carefully to her story and Priscilla and Grace asked her directly if all of these happenings had affected her work?

"Probably not until last week when I just got too involved with George or 'GL' as I called him."

At that point, I spoke up: "I'm sure that the three of us are sorry about your experience with Spielman which, in a way, is none of our business. What you do in your private time is none of our business unless it affects your performance here . . . and it seems to be doing just that. Whether or not it affects Spielman, we do not know, but you may be sure we'll investigate!" I then turned to Grace to ask, "What about mastering the Frieden calculator? Do you want to talk to Lennie about that?"

Grace spoke up, "Lennie, do you recall that I spoke with you about the sloppy work you did on one batch of the cost sheets?"

"Yes, and I wouldn't listen. I was wrong, probably distracted. But I'm ready for some more lessons; maybe Charlie could tutor me."

Grace glanced at me and asked, "What do you think, Roy?" I looked her in the eye and asked, "Can you spare Charlie for an hour or two next Monday and Tuesday?" Then I went on to observe, I think Lennie should be given a vacation for the rest of this week so she can rest up. What do you think of that, Lennie?"

Lennie was somewhat flustered, responding, "I can't afford to take a vacation."

"Don't worry about that; you'll not lose your salary, but I think that you can't afford *not* to take the time off!"

Priscilla intervened, "With all that's happening in your family, Lennie, can you find space to be yourself?"

"Yes. My husband's moved out, and I could bring my sister over to stay with me. Yeah, I think I am OK on that score! I guess I have to admit that I need some rest."

When we stood up and were all smiles, Lennie spoke up, "You're being more than fair, thank you all." She turned and left quickly.

"Whhhheeeewwww," Priscilla whistled, and nodded.

I looked at Grace and said, "Would you get me George Lincoln Spielman on the phone at the Gear Department?"

"What can you do about him?" Grace asked.

"I don't know but we'll soon find out! Make sure that Lennie has gone home."

Twenty minutes later, "George Lincoln ("GL" to Lennie) Spielman showed up, and we went immediately to the conference room. He looked frightened, but he could have been no more frightened than I.

I spent five minutes telling him what I knew and what he was alleged to have done. As might have been expected, he denied having tried to rape her. I also accused him of lying to her and inferred his deceiving me by taking Maryllyn and me to dinner even as he was two-timing his wife. I concluded, "What do you think I should do?"

Very nervous as he began to speak, he denied everything. I listened carefully, trying to hold my anger. When he'd finished,

I coolly remarked, "I don't know why you want to lie to me. I'm not questioning your motives; I'm questioning the propriety of your acts. I don't know if Lennie will try to sue you. I don't know that you, a so-called man of the world, have any idea of what you did and how you did it. I'm tempted to tell you to quit at the Gear Job and go back to New York . . ."

At the pause, he broke in, "You can't prove that I've not done my job."

"I'm not so sure, but right now I want you to get your ass out of here . . . right now. And you'd better fly straight and get no more ideas for plucking off any more women in this whole damn factory or lying to any of my colleagues! And you'd better damn well know that I'll be watching your performance on this Project . . . and watching closely!"

With that, he grabbed his notebook, flew out the door.

I was emotionally drained so I spent the rest of the afternoon with Thomas Mann's *The Magic Mountain*! Occasionally I'd peek at the German vocabulary on which I was boning up for the Harvard Language Exams.

159

24. *THE MAGIC MOUNTAIN*

Opening on Wednesday morning, I ran over the day's appointments and other details just before Grace and Priscilla checked in. When they stood by my desk, I reviewed the objective for the day, then I casually asked if they'd had any reactions to yesterday's events. Both said they'd had phone calls from Lennie. Priscilla observed that Loraine was still a bit teary, was very apologetic, but thanked her for a continuation of their friendship and support. Grace also said that Lennie thanked her for coming to her rescue, knowing she might just as easily been fired. Both indicated that she was "grateful for the way you handled what could have been a more terrifying incident."

"Did either of you ask if Lennie was thinking of taking George to the law?"

"I did," Priscilla said, "and she thought that that would make things worse. She said she wanted to get her divorce behind her and get on with her life. And you know, Roy, Lennie has always been what I'd call 'the bubbly type.' I don't forgive GL for doing what he did, but I can see how she might have given him the wrong signals."

Grace reinforced Priscilla's observations but went on to say, "How are we going to avoid a collision if Lennie and George meet here some day?"

"I don't think we need worry about it," I said, "I was pretty rough on him. If there is a confrontation while I'm out in the shops, one of you get her into your Rest Room and the other phone the Shop Police. And let me know as soon as possible. I think that GW has been warned sufficiently, but I'm prepared to get his a— out of here and call his company to make sure he goes. I'm keeping notes on yesterday's meeting and would appreciate your keeping whatever notes we might need if an emergency arises.

"What can I do, Roy?"

"Priscilla, I'd appreciate your reviewing GW's cost sheets to make a guesstimate of how far along he is in completing work on the Gear Job; also I'd appreciate your making a rough analysis of the approximate percentage of the gear work that's left to be done.

"If we need to consult Al Calligan about it, I'll have you get him on the phone, Grace. We're getting close to the last month's work as we planned it. If necessary, we can pull him from Gear and assign an appropriate engineer to finish his work. I certainly don't want him to feel that he's indispensable and blackmail us into keeping him. I'm pretty sure that Black and Kettley would support that kind of action if it became necessary. My worst fear: that this event with Lennie will breed rumors and run through the shops like the flu! As you know, not everybody loves our engineers."

Both women assured me that they would not feed such an epidemic and would have the figures I needed before the morning was over.

I needed the balance of the morning to "regroup" and make a mental list of Problems, Planning and Promises. In fact I was so pre-occupied with details for winding up my commitment, phase-out of Saco-Lowell and plan for the move to Cambridge, that I was almost surprised to hear a knock at the conference room door. I looked up to see Fritz Zimmerman standing there and hollered, "Come in," beckoning him with my free hand.

"Hi, Fritz!"

He shuffled over to the table where I was working and uttered his quiet, "Good noon-time, Roy." He then laid his familiar roll of prints and patents on my table, sat down rather gently in the rickety old chair that we'd rustled out of the closet a few months before, took out his bag lunch, waited for me to extract mine from my lunch bag and we both began to eat.

"Shall I talk while we eat?" he asked.

"Why not, Fritz, if it doesn't give you indignation!"

"He smiled in his quiet way, then began unrolling his roll of documents where he could refer to them and I could follow the pencil he was using as a pointer."

I arranged my position so I could see what he was talking about. It was, indeed, a continuation of the lecture he'd given Maryllyn and me (mostly ME!) in his room after our dinner awhile back. He was precise, avoided the math which he'd poured into my dead ears before, and got to some of the key points in the inventing process at which he'd had to devise cams which he said had never been used on such machines before. This time also, he had brought photos which reflected those critical points wherein planing metal on a curve cut huge shavings that were very visible and cogent in reflecting both power and precision. I was very impressed. Too, he had both drawings and photos of those huge propellers being keyed onto the drive shafts.

At this point I asked Fritz, "How do you know what to use for materials to make keys to keep all the parts together without having the keys sheered?"

"Good question, good problem, Roy, and not easily solved. As you may well imagine, we used trial and error as our methodology, even after employing all the data we had on tensile strengths and various data on a variety of metals. We finally concluded that in a worst-case scenario, we could weld the propeller and shaft together. After all, if a ship ran ashore, the entire mechanism might need that kind of treatment on a beach off Saigon, Tokyo or wherever."

When Fritz began re-rolling his papers, I knew he'd concluded the second part of his lecture. As I held out my hand and started to thank and congratulate him, he surprised me with a question: "You know, Roy, I've seen Thomas Mann's *The Magic Mountain* sitting there on your desk for all the weeks I've been here, and I wonder if you know what it means to me?"

"No, Fritz, I would have no way of knowing that."

"Probably not since I've not mentioned it to anybody since I arrived in June. But, it does because . . ." and I almost fainted as he stopped, became emotional for at least thirty seconds, wiped his nose with a Kleenex from the box on my desk, then continued.

"Sorry," he mumbled unobtrusively, "you see . . . long ago when I first came to this country and after I'd been exposed to tuberculosis, I was diagnosed as having t.b. I was almost through with my engineering education. Doctors said I should enter a sanatorium or I might die before it was under control. I was terribly run down from going to school and working full time. I fought against going to such a place as a sanatorium because I'd heard what horrible places they were to leave! But I finally succumbed and went to one in New Hampshire. I'd heard of Mann's book, had purchased a copy, but never had time to read it. But when I got to the place I had feared, I began reading it, actually in German. I read it slowly; and, whereas in my early days there I wanted to get back to my life, I began to feel as Catsorp did . . . I didn't care if I didn't go back."

163

I broke in on his story, "In short, you identified with Cat-sorp."

"Precisely!"

"I would never have known this, Fritz, I had no idea!"

"In other words, you know why I broke down a few seconds ago and perhaps why I'm sensitive about being slow . . . as John MacScott observed. Also, at that time I felt very 'sorry for myself,' kept asking, 'Why *me*?'"

"Yes," I said and slowed the discussion and began to feel badly about having misjudged him. I spoke up again, "Fritz, did you ever tell MacScott that story?"

"No, Roy, I've never told anybody that story since I got out of the sanatorium and worked in the engineering world. Most engineers are too case-hardened to identify with it. I'm not sure if I'd have ever had courage to tell you if I hadn't seen the Mann book here on your table or on your desk in the other room. One more point; you're not the engineering type. I figure you as being a humanities guy, more interested in Shakespeare and American history than engineers. And I say that in praise rather than criticism. Whenever I get together with my engineer colleagues, we talk about you, how you react to our problems, what you say. Naturally, my situation with MacScott and GW's with Calligan have been discussed, in our cars, in our rented apartments, here in the shops from time to time. Since we're solvers of math, physics and practical engineering problems, we tend to think that engineering way. But we marvel how Saco-Lowell managed to find you for this coordination job."

By this time I was feeling uncomfortable with what might have been perceived as flattery, but I was fascinated by the coincidence around *The Magic Mountain*. I knew he was sincere and I should not simply reject his compliments like water off a duck's back. So I returned to his experience at the sanatorium:

"Fritz was your sanatorium experience as bad as you had been given to believe that it would be? And was your gradual thinking about remaining *in* or getting *out* of the sanatorium similar to Catsorp's?"

"Similar, Roy, but not quite the same. My experience in New Hampshire was one of foothills. I think that Hans was fortunate to be in high mountains. It may be corny but I think he had more experience of the very highs and very lows of one's perspective. That may be simplistic psychology, but it's the way I view it in retrospect."

"One other question, Fritz, what happened when you returned to 'real life' with its everyday problems, you know, putting food on the table, changing diapers . . . ?"

Fritz cut me off. "Roy, I had no family. I was alone and continue to be so. But I kept busy, lived alone but was never lonely. There were too many 'impossible' problems to solve, ocean-going ships that needed their propellers planed, too many aerodynamic problems to be solved in the airplane industry, and so on. I always had a steady job to put the proverbial bread on the table. At night, I worked on those problems on my own drafting board. I eschewed card games, billiards and other such pastimes. I might go to a Yankees-Red Sox game, but I was never a 'fan' as in fanatic! And I enjoyed solving problems. For instance, Roy, I can see problems in the textile world that haven't been solved. How do I know? Because I've taken advantage of being here in Biddeford to take the regular tours through the Pepperell and ask as many questions as politeness allowed us to ask. A couple of times I've been the only one on tour and that meant that the floor was open for meaningful questions, at least 'meaningful for me.' Also, thanks to your textile library just downstairs, I've borrowed the manuals for all the machines that Saco-Lowell makes and found it fascinating to read what the writers of those manuals say about the problems solved by each succeeding model. That's where my world starts, but like all engineering, it will probably never *end* there."

I took a look at the clock, noted that it was two o'clock and I had promised to visit the Wood Department and that I'd better pause to phone to change my appointment. "What is John Mac-Scott going to say when you show up late?"

"That's easy," Fritz retorted, "You could write me an excuse slip or I can tell him that you kept me after school!"

"Glad to see that the sanatorium and engineering lives haven't destroyed your sense of humor, Fritz! Incidentally, didn't I hear you swapping puns with your friends the other day?"

Fritz was sharp, replying, "I love puns! Everybody has a good time where there's punning: those who invent them have fun and those who frown and growl and 'boo' have fun, so everybody has a good time."

"Fritz, we seem to have derived that conclusion independently!"

"No, Roy, I was simply quoting you," and he shuffled away laughing!

It left me scratching my head and asking myself, "When and where did I say *that*?"

25. NIGHT ENERGIES TO THE SKIES

Somewhere between mail at home or random comments at the shops, the words, "Sweetser Home" bounced out of the word crib. I think it came from Alfred Alquin, an engineer who had driven around the Sweetser Home grounds in Saco. First thing one morning, he asked me about the place and its function. Although I was not up-to-date on the Home's current status, I'd lived near it growing up in Saco and passed it many times as a boy when hiking the old Eastern Railroad track on the way to our muddy swimming hole in Goose Fare Brook.

Once I'd plunged into the topic, the vistas of memory became clearer. I told him who Sweetser, the Saco shoe manufacturer, was and how he had left his fortune to several Saco charitable societies at the time of his death and that Sweetser Home was the refuge for many orphans from various parts of the State of Maine. Too, I told him my Sweetser schoolmates' stories and their vivid descriptions of lurid chapters of the Home's history, especially regarding a man named Tom who punished the "inmates" in ways that made Dickens' descriptions of English orphans of the nineteenth century seem almost benevolent. And probably, judging from my dad's conversation with this Tom when he came to dad's garage to have his van-like truck inspected, he thought of himself as "benevolent." A biased spectator might have charged, "benevolent dictator."

During my conversation with Alquin, however, and to keep the topic relevant to Saco-Lowell Shops, I explained to him what some of us had been doing to aide the war effort. Early in the war, as part of "civil defense," the local civil/civic defense authorities enlisted cooperation from the Shops where a coordinator was set up to work out schedules, primarily for the night shift at the Sweetser Watch Tower. Although we accepted the more or less permanent night schedule, I do recall pinch-hitting for another person in our department when he ran into a family conflict. We exchanged the 2-to-4 and 4-to-6 shifts. After doing this, I wished I'd been able to take the 4-6 shift permanently. It tore less from one's body *not* to get up in the middle of the night, confront the vagaries of the weather, especially in the winter, then return home and even try to go back to sleep for an hour or so. But this experience did sensitize me to firemen's, police and various industrial schedules as well as my father-in-law's as he worked alternating night and day shifts at the power-generating plant at the foot of Dean's Hill in Biddeford.

I know not which, if any, other local agencies or companies were consulted about aviation surveillance, but no doubt they needed a fairly light-free area from which to observe the skies. Sweetser provided that protection and permitted construction of a wooden look-out tower on their highest point of land, a tower which local citizens staffed and watched the skies twenty-four hours a day to report (via phone) to local aviation authorities any air traffic, referenced the planes to that Saco point, and reported the approximate height and type of plane anybody might see at any time of day or night. I remember spotting only one small plane during the several months that I served.

Even though I was working the proverbial 25-hour day at Saco-Lowell in the Winter of '43–'44, I vividly recalled setting the alarm clock at 1:00 AM, rising slowly in the cold and riding my bike (when the snow was not too deep) or walking the 1.5 miles to the tower, climbing the wooden steps to the top, lifting the trap door to crawl up into the warm room, chatting with my friends on the 12-to-2 shift, then scanning the skies from 2-to-4. Some nights I didn't even bother to go to bed; fortunately my duty occurred only one night a week. I might stay up and read before leaving for the tower; then, once back at home read some more until time to wake up our 1-1/2 year old daughter or stick a bottle in her mouth, eat breakfast, pack my bag lunch quickly, and take off for the shops and not see my family again until evening.

At the time, I felt that Saco-Lowell employees were making an important contribution to the war effort. During that period, however, I was shifted from one Draft allocation to another, from 1-A, to 2-B and 2-A, then back to 3-A, etc. I experienced such a state of uncertainty, it sometimes felt as though I were caught whirling in a revolving door. When finally taking an Army physical and being "slapped" into 1-A, but failing the stiff Navy physical as well as asking too many questions of the Colonel in charge, I never actually got started in the Japanese Language program at the U of Colorado. Hence when the Local Draft Board allowed me to return to industry via a 4-F assignment, I dropped all pretenses of enthusiasm about war work and got admitted to Harvard Graduate School of Arts and Sciences, the month before I was drawn back into Saco-Lowell in May, 1944.

One chilling footnote to the brief encounter with the Japanese language program: the group of naval officers, with whom I would have served, was alleged to have been killed by a Japanese kamikaze plane as they prepared to go ashore at Okinawa. I've attempted to confirm this, but have never had the opportunity to do the research in Naval records in Washington to verify the event. But it does send chills up my back when I contemplate the possibility of that fate.

26. FLIRTING WITH DANGER

One morning when things were going fairly smoothly (the engineers had gone into the shops, the Friedens were humming smoothly, and Grace, Priscilla and I had gone off on some personal tangent or other), Priscilla asked, "Roy, are you keeping a diary these days? I know you used to in past years."

"Not systematically, sis, just a burst of words here and just a burst there . . . too much happening and too fast to record much of it in detail!"

She followed up, "But, Roy, what we're doing is historical if not hysterical, as you might joke; you may never know when you may want to talk or write about the Shops. Since you've never had such a unique opportunity to see the total operation, isn't it time to take time for notes now?"

Grace chipped in with the thought that "You can't tell when you might use such observations at Graduate School."

I retorted with the observation, "Assuming I go!" I paused a moment, debated whether or not I should say anything about Mark Black's urging me to delay going or even take steps to seize upon Saco-Lowell opportunities.

Priscilla scowled and remarked, "Come on, brother, you want to become a college professor; don't muff it!"

Grace nodded, "I agree. I've been married to a life-long Saco-Lowell employee, and know that it's no picnic!"

I thanked them. They went back to their paper work, and I stared out the window over the shop roofs toward Pepperell's red brick buildings and mused for a few minutes. I then took a walk to the east end of our building, stared at the narrow, corrugated bridge that connected the Saco and Biddeford plants, kept on walking to the end of the building where I could stand unnoticed and stare down river, across the Pepperell vistas at the 200-foot chimney that carried generator fumes into the sky. Also spied a few small boats motoring below the falls. Then, as always I felt a deep sense of nostalgia spying the distant east bank of the river, near my birthplace and my grandmother's home from which as a boy I watched river traffic in coal, oil and lumber, also outboard motor boat races, featuring my favorite outboard speedboat, "Miss Betty."

I mused on other thoughts such as Priscilla's and Grace's viewpoints to add to Maryllyn's and my deliberations: "Torn as I am, I'm sure that Saco-Lowell is a dead-end for me since I can't abide by so many of the negatives. Also, it's becoming too late to change plans now. And staying here would make our housing transition to Harvard more difficult in mid-winter. Helpful as Mark Black has been to us, Maryllyn and I had best make a final decision soon, then I'll inform him next week of our decision."

I gradually strolled back to the office, stopping at Grace's and Priscilla's back-to-back desks to say, "Thank you for your encouragement this morning." I did not tell them how I was leaning, but I saw them look at one another and smile as though they felt my leanings.

Back at my desk, I stared out the window, picked up my pen and began to put my image-making mind to work re: some of the "sights and sounds" that I'd encountered over the years at S-L-S, trying to avoid heavy issues and/or conflicts. Some of my notes to myself:

171

. . . rhythmic hammer blows on a packing boxes being made to ship textile parts across the world;

. . . similar rhythms, in ker-plunk, ker-plunk raps as a stamping machine grinds out standard 3/4" washers;

. . . pounding of a gigantic machine forcing air into the chambers of a pneumatic drill digging a ditch for a new water or electric line;

. . . cranes whinnying overhead in the yard dropping "tons" of scrap metal with a *crash* into the blast furnace;

. . . tearing and ripping sounds as men and women open boxes in the receiving room, exercising their curiosity and pencils to record what came from where;

. . . rumbling of a tractor along a wooden ramp or across the connector bridge with a load of empty barrels;

. . . feeling the heat, even at a distance, as the half-naked foundry workers catch the red-hot slag in their long-handle dippers as it pours out of the furnaces;

. . . acrid smoke rising from the moulds as the cast iron cools;

. . . clouds of dust filling the snagging rooms where men look like coal miners;

. . . the smell and taste of that dust;

. . . the cleaner smell of shavings and sawdust cut from a variety of woods such as birch and pine being processed in the wood departments;

. . . the contrasting odors of varnish, banana oil and shellac in the painting departments . . .

The phone rang, Grace answered, passed it across the desk, whispering, "It's for you, Mark Black."

I stopped scribbling and said, "Hello, Mr. Black, what can I do for you?"

"Roy, we need to settle your departure situation. Can you come over?"

172

"Could you give me five or ten minutes."

He responded, "Sure, that's OK!"

I asked Grace, "Would you try to get Maryllyn on the phone?"

As she called the Trull Hospital to reach Maryllyn, I made some notes for myself to work into the "sights and sounds" piece, then sat back in my chair, took a quick glance at *The Magic Mountain* on the corner of my desk, slid it into my desk drawer, then closed my eyes to compose my brief message to Mark Black.

Maryllyn was soon on the phone.

"Hi, dear, sorry to bother you, but I've been summoned by Mark Black regarding a decision to go to graduate school or remain here for at least a few months to help finish this project. But, I also talked with Priscilla and Grace this morning; they agree with you! We should go!"

Maryllyn was somewhat restrained and low key, so I knew that she was speaking from a public place because she quietly asked, "Are you sure?"

"Yes, we've wavered on the issue too long! To go? To stay? To go? Etc! And this morning I went through the pangs of imagining how difficult it would be to make this shift in January. We surely can't remain where we are nor stay with your folks indefinitely. So, I guess it makes more sense to go in October; after all, we've paid two months rent in Arlington and have an entry date at Harvard."

Maryllyn, seeming relieved, said, "OK with me, dear! I've got to go; have a patient waiting."

I said, "Great! See you tonight," and hung up.

Grace and Priscilla looked up and said, almost in unison, "I'm glad!"

It all happened pretty fast so I made my ten-minute deadline to see Mark Black.

As I entered, he was his usual genial self, dismissed his secretary, Ethel, working in one corner of his office, and I stole a quick glance thru the multiple window panels that separated Black's office and the List and Specification Departments which he supervised. They all seemed busily engaged with their work, but I waved anyway.

"Well, Roy, what's the verdict?"

"I've decided to go back to college in late October. There are many reasons for it. Much as I know that I'd make an OK, lifelong Saco-Lowell man; and, much as I appreciate your encouragement, I think that I'd better try the academic adventure. Since I taught Sunday School at the Saco Methodist Church a few years ago, I've had a hankering to try it at the college or university level. My professors at Bates said they thought I had the intelligence and the personal skills to do it. I know it's going to be a difficult time economically; you know my economic and social heritage. Yet, once I've set mind and jaw to do something, I usually get it done."

"Yes, Roy, I know that, but I why do you want to begin graduate school facing those economic hardships?"

"I agree that it will not be easy, but the Bates challenge was similar; and, thanks to you, giving me an opportunity to work vacations and summers, plus Maryllyn's nursing, helped us make it."

"Well, Roy, what about staying here until January or June before beginning graduate school?"

"Maryllyn and I have run that exhaustively through our list of options, but our housing situation here and in Cambridge will not be too easy. Rentals around Harvard are rising; and just in case, we put a two-month deposit on an apartment in Arlington."

"So you'd already made your decision when you went to Boston a few week ends ago?"

"Not really. That was a 'What if?' decision that depended upon family assistance, our willingness to forfeit two months of rent as well as Harvard's willingness to accept me dating back to my interview with the dean last April . . . before I came back to Saco-Lowell in May and we started the cost job. I have a hunch that it may be more difficult to gain admission when the war is over and soldiers return to continue with their careers."

"Well, Roy, I'll support your decision. I know that you're bright, loyal, a hard-working and determined guy. Naturally, I'll try to assist you during the summers and will monitor your progress. We have already contacted Freddie Cote who is willing to pick up the reins of the Cost Job where you drop them so long as he has a couple of weeks before you leave, around October 10 if that's OK with you."

I thanked Black profusely, promised to be back to him again regarding the transition leading to my exit.

As I left the office and looked down thru the Specs and List Departments, two or three persons waved. I made an abbreviated wave back, went out Black's main door and simply walked around to enter via the other route and speak for just a minute to those who had waved. By this time Black had left his office, probably to go down to report to V.P. Kettley. I had no intention of announcing my decision to my old friends. I knew that the news would travel fast enough, once Black's Secretary Ethel had taken dictation, putting the plan into effect.

I ambled back to the office via the Rest Room, which, fortunately, was empty. No temptation to talk there!

Walking into the office, I encountered Charlie leaving: "Gotta noon dental appointment," he said; and, I recalled that he had asked for permission to leave early.

"Hope it's less painful than getting hit with that line drive in Yankee Stadium, " I mused.

175

"Nothing's ever been more painful than that!" he exclaimed. "But I'm still glad to be here."

I chuckled and went back to my desk. With a half hour to go before noon, I related our decision to both Grace and Priscilla, "Everything's OK! We'll talk later" and sat down to continue my scribbling. Actually, it was both challenging and fun to record those smells, sounds and sights:

. . . flashing red signal lights in a dark corridor as a phone operator attempts to locate a foreman;

. . . flying flags on three mastheads at the highest point on the Shops buildings, the Minuteman for official war bonds, the Army-Navy "E" for excellence and Old Glory for hope, justice and the traditions of America . . . all very colorful when the clouds peeled away and the sky turned deep blue;

. . . men and women applying various gauges held by toughened but sensitive fingers to guarantee quality of work;

. . . and at the office level the specter of men (few women did this work) leaning on drafting tables beneath vapor fluorescent lights, some of them usually buzzing as these light sources burned out.

As I reviewed this list of sights, sounds, smells, tastes and surging of feelings that any one person might experience in an ordinary day, I knew that I had barely scratched the proverbial surface; but I also knew that most observers of the scene could easily extrapolate their senses to locate the danger zones such as the slapping leather belts: one need not watch them long without *knowing* what happens when humans tangled with that noise and power.

Upon pausing, I heard the noon whistles blowing, waved to the office group as they rushed off to lunch, then sat back in my swivel chair to yawn and say to myself, "What a morning!"

27. "E" AS IN "EXCELLENCE"

Grace started the day by asking me about "E" day at S-L-S. She said that one of the engineers had asked her about it. She'd heard husband Rusty talk about it, but they'd been out of town on that celebrative day so didn't have much first-hand information. What could I tell her?

I hadn't been too impressed by the PR about it, but I did save the *Biddeford Daily Journal* about that special day and would bring it in. When I learned that it was "GL" who wanted to know about the special day, I sought him out to review it with him, never mentioning the Lennie Incident. A few days later when he returned from the Gear Job early and was working on his parts sheets, I picked up the newspaper, went to his table to lay it out so he could see it for himself. I looked over his shoulder as he read and pointed out that the paper carried the four-page spread six days following the Event.

I also pointed out that there was much preparation and publicity around the Saco-Lowell's celebrating the Army-Navy's awarding the factory as recognition of its contribution to the war effort. I started to say "earned" the award, but GL looked up sidewise as if to ask, "earned?"

I looked down the page with him without further comment. I had my own reservations so I wondered what his might be? But he read on aloud and I followed:

"THE ARMY-NAVY PRODUCTION AWARD
FOR EXCELLENCE IN WAR PRODUCTION
  TO THE
MEN AND WOMEN
 OF SACO-LOWELL SHOPS
BIDDEFORD, MAINE
MARCH 16, 1943"

The announcement was followed by a quote from General Douglas MacArthur: "There can be no line of demarcation between the man who uses a weapon and the man who makes it. If one fails, the other must perish." The General's quote was followed by one by a S-L-S official:

". . . and our answer is, We will not fail, for we who make weapons have a task easy by comparison, with those who have been called upon to use them.

"In being awarded the Army-Navy 'E' the men and women at the Saco Lowell Shops may feel justly proud that their work has deserved such recognition. But we also know that while the 'E' Stands for Excellence, it does not stand for Sacrifice . . . the kind of Sacrifice our men on the fighting fronts are making. This award, representing work which has been done, will be a symbol of the greater work that will continue to be done until there is more than enough material for victory. This is our pledge to those who are sacrificing their all and serving with the colors everywhere."

This was hardly a surprising statement being made in the tradition of wartime patriotism or even echoing the words of Abraham Lincoln at Gettysburg when observing the dedication of "a portion of that field as a final resting place for those who here gave their lives that that nation might live. . . ."

The *Journal* went on to pay tribute to the people of Saco-Lowell at a "distinguished gathering" and with "impressive ceremonies" that included patriotic music by the military band, appropriate speeches by Army and Navy officers, Saco-Lowell officials and culminated in raising the "E" insignia over the highest roof of the textile machine plant. All of this was documented with three pages of photographs of everyday workers, twenty employees with 40-63 years of service, and a full array of some one hundred apprentices and company officers at their Ninth Annual Banquet. In addition, six South American companies were depicted as customers.

In short, it was a notable celebration of the company's part in the War. Production was stopped during the ceremony so that all workers could attend if they so wished. From that day on, the company flew the "E" banner daily along side the American and company flags. No doubt most employees wore their "E" pins proudly, I kept mine, but only recently gave it to the Saco Museum as a WWII artifact.

When GL finished reading and surveying the picture, he looked up and said, "You were there, what do you think?"

I paused a few moments, then he broke in to say, "OK, I know that you probably cannot say exactly what you think."

"That's not quite so," I began. "I owe little fealty to S-L-S in the narrow sense. I usually express my opinion, no matter the situation. For most people attending, it was probably a proud moment of their lives. For those of us who took a broader view, no doubt it was a good PR event. It so happens, George, that I did write something about it at the time and I brought it along today, figuring you might ask me a question like that!"

So I read from the journal that I'd written the day following the event; at least I read most of it, slowly, since I'd not had time to think it through very thoroughly.

"During World War II the military forces attempted to boost industrial morale and production by holding E-days at various company plants around the U.S.A. Such a day was held yesterday at S-L-S at the Biddeford-Saco plant. At that time Saco-Lowell was manufacturing anti-aircraft gun controls in a subcontract with Bendix Aviation, making aluminum tubes/fuses for Naval depth charges assembled at Sylvania Electric as part of the anti-submarine phase of the war. They were also assembling bogey wheels (or carriages) for the Ford Motor Company's Bren Gun Carrier as well as other smaller sub-contract jobs. These products are being done under the surveillance (quality control) of U. S. Government Agencies.

"On that 'great day' of celebration, yesterday, there were the usual flowery and flattering speeches, the hoisting of American and 'E-for-Excellence' flags, the stiff March winds flapping them atop the highest buildings on both sides of the river. In addition to a military band, there appeared Army and Navy military officers as well as top Saco-Lowell officials. The CEO of the Saco-Biddeford plant, R. A. Kettley, served as master of ceremonies while the Superintendent of the Biddeford Plant, Jim Crosby [whom you met at least once, George, at the Gear Job office for that notorious meeting with Al, the Foreman; I looked up and George shook his head, still in disbelief] accepted the 'E' banner as it was hoisted to the masthead. I'll always remember, too, that the manufacturing and office procedures shut down so that everybody who wanted to attend could do so if so moved. [I recall a few of my office mates *not* attending with an excuse, "too cold a wind!"]

"I think that most of my officemates recognized the occasion as a patriotic gesture as well as a symbolic support for the war effort. Each of us was given a sterling 'E' pin whether or not he or she was actually engaged in manufacturing war products. Each also received a Certificate of Appreciation."

When I paused toward the end of my journal quotation,

George said, "But you've still not said what you thought about the affair!"

"I concur, but let me read a little more from my notes." So I continued: "I certainly did not buy into the patriotism nor PR aspects of the event. But I did recognize the reality of need to keep people on the job at a difficult phase of the war. I simply don't know how many people were or even now are involved, directly or indirectly, in producing the implements of war. I do know that all I hear is 'bitch-bitch-bitch' about security, eternal waiting and frustration over the delayed delivery of both new machines and critical tools, extra-long days and black-out curtains, unreal shortages of sugar, gasoline and meat . . . which to me has little to do with Saco-Lowell Shops' production."

I looked up from my diary/log and looking George straight in the eye, I added, "I know that my viewpoint as well as that of many of my colleagues is very cynical because everyday we are privy to so many wasted materials and energies that it seems ridiculous to reward a company for such incompetence. You've seen it yourself as you've picked and poked through tool cribs in the Gear Department and it would surprise me if you and your engineering colleagues haven't seen the waste and incompetence, too!"

George retorted. "I concur with your perspective and your cynicism and might feel the same. I've encountered it on other war projects across the country. But there's one more piece of short-sightedness of which *you* are a part!"

"What's that?" I asked, as casually as possible."

George was crystal clear, "You are part of a process that I think the company will eventually regret. We are writing history whereas I think that we should be helping with planning for the future. In fact, that was one of the causes of the impasse which brought out Al's anti-Semitism at the Gear Job."

181

"George, I couldn't agree with you more; and, as you may know, some of your colleagues have raised the same issue. And I doubt that the Saco-Lowell policy managers will recognize that until the war is over. I suspect, as I indicated the first time I met you and your colleagues back in June, that the tactics and strategy of what we are doing reflects an accountant's expedient hunch about what may work with the Office of Price Administration.. And while we certainly haven't used your knowledge and skills to the max on this project . . . and while I have sensed your frustration even when you've not always expressed it, I suspect that the chosen plans and procedures may be easier to 'sell' OPA than it would if we'd mixed the two processes."

George reflected for a moment, then said, "I'd not quite seen it like this before, but your argument is surely cogent. "

With one last response, I added, "May I suggest that to your closing report or summary of your work here, when this job IS HISTORY, that you attach to your written statement your comments about how you perceive this issue. Also, please include any specific recommendations for modification of any particular part or assembly!"

George thanked me for my describing the "Excellence Day" and for my opinions of what the day was all about.

As I reflected upon this encounter with George, I wondered if George might have a different opinion of Saco-Lowell and me if I'd described the "civil defense" programs in which S-L-S employees had served as organizers for various "civil defense" programs, especially the one headed by a prominent WWI military officer, Col. Harry Goodier, Paymaster at Saco-Lowell. He organized and developed various groups responsible for informing citizens of dangers and emergencies in the event of land or sea incursions on our local coast.

But this entire segment of "civil defense" might not have

happened as it did, if not for Saco-Lowell. As I recalled, that war effort was honored in some other public manners. I doubt whether I would serve in such a "civil defense" role in today's climate of war.

28. FROM THE HORSE'S MOUTH

A day or two after my "interview" with Mark Black, I screwed my courage to the time-clock machine, observing that I had only a short time left to gain insights from new sources, and phoned Al Stuart, Chief Accountant, who had been brought in when R. A. Kettley became CEO of manufacturing at the consolidation of the various Massachusetts and Maine plants. I was nervous in calling him, although Mark had recommended it. Al had been very cool to me since I had refused to participate in his closeted "homo group" some years before. Yet, I thought that he might be willing to talk since the recommendation was from Mark Black, probably with the backing of Kettley. Anyway, I called. After reaching two or three in his hierarchy of assistants, he said "Hello?"

I began, "Hello, Al, this is Roy, Roy Fairfield. I am calling at Mark Black's suggestion. He thinks that you may have some valuable insights that relate to this Special Cost Project on which I've been working all summer."

"Yes," he began rather coolly. "I was bound to know what you were doing since you, Black and Kettley stole some of my department's authority right out from under my nose."

I retorted, "Yes, I've wondered about that, but I've been in no position to question their decisions to take what action they took in setting up the cost project last Spring although RAK said it had your approval."

"Yeah," observed Al, "And I now hear that you're going to steal another of my men to finish up what you're dropping to go to Harvard to get a PhD. Incidentally, I think that that's a stupid idea; some of the most stupid people I've ever met in this business have their stupid doctor's degrees."

"OK, Al, I hear you loud and clear, but Black and Kettley think that you could provide an angle of vision that nobody else in the Shops could provide and asked that I talk with you. I'm simply following up their suggestions."

There was a long pause on the phone before he finally spoke, "Well, I guess I have to do what the bosses tell me to do. I always have. But I am sure you'll not like all that you hear. We can meet in the conference room in an hour if that's OK with you. I'll bring some of my notes."

"Fine with me, see you in an hour."

He kept the appointment. When he strolled in, wearing his usual simple costume, a white shirt with a loosely-arranged, four-in-hand tie, baggy black slacks, quite proper for a S-L-S mid-management attire. I held out my hand and he coolly took it as he laid down three large loose-leaf notebooks, filled to overflowing. We sat down at the conference table, and he pointedly stared at me to ask, in a rather brusque manner, "What do I know that you don't?"

"Probably lots since you've been here longer and had more responsibility than I. But there are some angles which I'd like to understand better."

"OK, which?" he asked, rather coolly.

"Well, I have some sense of the problems related to the consolidation, for instance a taste of the matter of excess repair parts and scrap iron, obsolete machine tools, and the phenomenon of building textile machines without contracts in the hope that some standard machines would sell after the war. Could you help with perspective on any or all of those issues as you see them from an accountant's viewpoint?"

"Sure, but you've combined into one question more topics than I used to cover in giving three graduate courses a semester in a School of Accounting in Boston. However, I can probably give you some overall insights relevant to Saco-Lowell and its complex history."

He then proceeded to illustrate his analyses via graphs, annual reports, and his own notes regarding the way that surpluses of spare parts had a negative impact upon profits and losses. This in turn affected the debt loads, which had occurred for many years. He also went into considerable detail about how all of these factors weighed heavily both before and after the consolidation. Too, he indicated how slowing sales in many parts of the textile industry and closing plants such as Amoskeag Manufacturing in New Hampshire during the Great Depression, kept the Shops in a perpetual bind.

I interjected in order to clarify: "In other words there was not enough production and sales control to manufacture in the black?"

"Exactly, that's a good summary."

"Well, tell me, Al, I hear rumors about President Edwards being either a genius or the fall guy when it comes to the renaissance of the Shops? Is it either-or or neither?"

Al went on, "I think there's no question that his bold step of consolidation as well as the brilliant financial reorganization of the corporation, saved the day. The Sales Division gained new perspectives and objectives. You are well aware of comparing Sales and List prices for the Comptroller; namely, David Edwards, because you did that for awhile before you deserted us and took off for Bates."

He looked up and scowled, reflecting his contempt for

higher education, but I didn't blink an eye as he continued, "And Roy, without all that tinkering which President Edwards did, making bold and necessary changes, Saco-Lowell might not have survived. If he hadn't done it, you know what might have happened to life in Saco and Biddeford life to say nothing about individuals' lives! If the changes had not been made, we might have folded as Amoskeag and other textile manufacturers at all levels did, both north and south."

He paused took a deep breath and asked, "I could use a cup of coffee, how about you?" I assented and he called in an assistant to get two cups of coffee and some coffee rolls.

I was pleasantly surprised, thanked him and said, "Ok, Al, Mark Black loaned me President Edwards' well-known Dec 15, 1927 'Letter to the Board of Directors' as well as Annual Reports from the 30's and early 40's. I've been reading them for the kind of insights and/or perspectives you've just afforded me."

As we drank the coffee and munched on the rolls, Al seemed to relax a little and asked, "Would you like some more of my perspectives, on both management and some of the mores of the Shops, some of which you may never have encountered?"

I was, of course, delighted that he'd broken through his negativism and other resistances to want to talk more.

Al went on, "You know, Roy, having been here about a decade and a half, I've seen lots of life come and go, also many changes." Pointing to his three thick notebooks, he remarked, "I've kept a lot of notes; I'm sure they'll never see the light of day in book form, but I don't mind quoting from them liberally. I'm sure that my insights are unique; also, the fact that I had secretarial help as well as knowing shorthand should give my observations more relevance and insights than as though I'd depended entirely upon memory."

I remained silent as Al picked up all three notebooks, broke the text open at points which he had marked with slips of paper, observing, "Don't try to take notes, Roy. So long as these note-books don't leave this room, I'll be glad for you to peruse them at your leisure. It will be my opportunity to get both this stuff and anger off my chest."

He picked up the first notebook, cut the thick text to his trigger slip and began reading about the slip-shod accounting of early mills in New England whereby "the directors decided that a certain percentage was a 'fair profit' for the year; they then charged to 'Plant' or credited the difference between costs and sales to the same account. Obviously," Al interjected, "it was too simplistic a practice until government tax laws introduced a percentage for depreciation, a practice continued into the 20th century. I was shocked," Al emphasized, "when one observer, describing these phenomena from the official record, wrote 'The Directors passed the usual dividend.' The ignorant bastard assumed that the Board passed and paid dividends whereas 'passed' meant that they did *not* pay them! This is only one example, and there were many more, where an accountant's view might have saved both money and embarrassment. The record is filled with such stupidity! And David Edwards had to deal with all those blunders."

Al went on to reference many other such misinterpretations as being sorry facts of Saco-Lowell's history. Although some of his critiques did not directly obtain to S-L-S, Al painted a gloomi-er picture than one might have expected when dealing with the history of the textile manufacturing business. In one instance there was a suit over a missing $200,000 involving the then-York Manufacturing Company as it consolidated. Al suggested to the lawyer involved in the specific situation that "possibly he would find the sales of coal [which York then handled] also included cloth (at no cost) to pad the profits; and, indeed, that's what the counsel discovered!" Al cited similar aberrations and manipulations of standard accounting principles applied to both Pepperell Manufacturing Company and Saco-Lowell Shops.

When I asked about his relationship with President Edwards, he pointed to a passage he'd written some years before, explaining to Edwards "that what I have to write is not in any sense a criticism of your wonderful work, nor to be taken as any contradiction—because naturally you have done more research than I. Also, whereas you have approached the history from a financial and business policy viewpoint, I have approached it from a 'people' view. What I've tried to do is to make the people live and to search beyond actions and policies of the person or condition that brought it about."

Al went on to speak like a historian's historian, saying that "Even as Procopius wrote two histories, one a pure historian's work and the other about the individuals, so possibly my own notes are a supplement to yours."

Following up on his claim to be "people" oriented, he confessed that the local Labor Unions had approached him during troubled times and asked him to lead them. Although Stuart seemed to have agonized over the conflict between himself as Chief Accountant and S-L-S management, he turned down the union offer in view of his years as part of management, observing that he could not switch sides because of his "long-based loyalties."

Stuart also stood by some of his opinions of people and expressed them clearly in his notes. He was hard on some his former Lowell, Massachusetts bosses, but in a strange sort of way, he really denuded some of the management folk with whom he'd had to contend. Somewhere in the middle of his quoting his notes, he asked if I'd ever heard of the Blake-Reynolds conflict. I said, "Heard of it as being 'classic' but have no details."

Then, Stuart opened up about E. E. Blake, Superintendent or managing chief of the Biddeford operation from 1904 until he'd died only recently. Stuart observed that he was regarded as a kindly, understanding old man, a grandfatherly type. But Al referred to his notes and was very candid. He observed that Blake "didn't get along well with newcomers, their most serious criticism being summed up in one phrase; namely, he was 'hell on putting things together close.'" Al went on to say that "the Shops needed flexibility, of which the veteran, Blake, had little. He was locked and blocked in history."

At this point of discussion, Al took out a red pen and marked a passage to which he said "You might want to return by yourself." I did, but the essence of his remarks was quite simple and humanistic; namely, Al observed, "Some day, modern scientific management is going to include the necessity for knowing when the human body wears out and feels the effect of disease." It seems that Blake, the old workhorse of forty years, had cancer of the prostate; he couldn't concentrate; he magnified trivia way out of proportion, exasperated his secretary by requiring that she re-type letters as many as twenty times, no matter how routine or important they might be. Stuart argued that "that might have been OK for legal, engineering or patent communications, but certainly not for a response to a dinner invitation. "

Al went on, "It became obvious that Blake was not able to deal with a fiery and somewhat erratic Southern inventor-textile administrator [Reynolds] whose main objective was to get his invention into remunerative production. Blake, a soft-spoken man, could not deal with Reynolds; and, unfortunately, the cancer spread to Blake's throat and he died. And was much bemoaned by every one who knew him. His wife soon followed."

Stuart continued, "But this all ties into a series of events wherein the Shops for a time were like a ship without a captain.

In a way nobody was certain who was in charge. 'Cap' Beecroft returned to England after a series of catastrophes in his family. Rod Tarr was not universally liked or appreciated. The Blake-Reynolds battle was still a sore on the body management. Banfield had deserted Saco-Lowell for Whitin Machine Works and seemed to have taken 'bushels' of blueprints with him (especially related to S-L-S's shift from cast iron to steel parts for some machines). Thanks to an all-night vigil of some minor clerks who had access to the vault, the blueprints went with Banfield. In fact, there were times that I was involved in important decision making even though I was much lower on the management totem pole and wasn't sure of my responsibility even though I'd been assured of a high position when I moved from Massachusetts to Maine . . . even though I didn't want to come.

"Then there was the matter of R. A. Kettley." When Al mentioned him, I held my breath for we were meeting only a room or two removed from Kettley's office, but Al was equally candid about the CEO of the Biddeford & Saco plant. Quoting from his notes, Al went on to say, "For all of his apparent coldness, he has been extremely tender-hearted . . . so much so it is almost pathological. I was perhaps the only one who fully realized this and rode rough-shod over his apparent cruelness, much to the oft-expressed annoyance of others on the scene. Perhaps this is why I got the reputation throughout the Shops that if no one could get Mr. Kettley to agree to some concession, that I probably could. With all the uncertainty around, as you can see, this has been a tough cross to bear!"

Al went on to describe Kettley's childhood, remarking that "his father was something of a martinet, for I think that the boy never knew how to release his spirits and play . . . his father forcing him to study and drill, study and drill. But in later days, he realized that he'd needed that discipline and came to worship his

191

father. When his father died, he went home to another state and went into virtual hibernation. And when he returned to Maine, he not only went into his office to mourn in his own way, his office was off bounds. No decisions, however important, came from him. Upon a couple of occasions when we went to his home for decisions in crucial matters, whoever went with me, usually Al Lawe, we found him picking raspberries and would not stop until we were 'impressed' to help him finish the job!

"Oh, one other flashback: at the time of his father's death, he was almost paralyzed about what to do and asked me if he should go to the funeral. I said 'Yes,' but he was reluctant to go. He'd never seen a man dead. He went, but his wife handled the family's social obligations.

"One other near debacle: the decades-long competition between Whitin Machine Works and Saco-Lowell never got more tense than it did when the Banfield 'case' went to court. For some reason the judge at court had little or no experience in such cases as patent theft but made his decision on moral grounds. There was evidence and inferences of 'theft' but not enough evidence to settle the case; the victory went to Whitin, rubbing salt into a wound.

"There's lots more in my notes, Roy; and as I said before, you're welcome to read or refer to them, but please do not take them out of this room. I'll put my private secretary, Ann Thompson, in charge; after you've finished on any given day (except a week end when Ann doesn't work), simply phone her.

"Oh, on the juicier side: be sure to read a few pages from this part of my notes," and he put his finger into the notebook in his hands and went on to cite two groups of pages, describing a bit about what I'd find.

"Here," he smiled as he chuckled, "you'll find the story of a group of women in my very department, coming to me to

describe what one of our foremen was doing week ends at parties at Biddeford Pool. It seems that they were forced to serve
both Saco-Lowell employees but also giving Navy Officers
guarding our Coast, other kinds of 'sexperience.'" He chuckled
again as he repeated his play on the word, "sexperience." "It
was coercion at its worst and you'll see how I handled that case
without a public explosion, concerned that the women in my
department would be fired if they blew it open.

"A similar situation arose when one of the second hands in
the Foundry smuggled in 'sex partners' at night. It's all here!" Al
stressed. "You'll also see what I thought of Ed Henry, whom I
called a 'busybody' at one point and a 'stool pigeon' at another.
He was supposedly Director of Office Management. He once
challenged me by sending the sister of one of his employee
friends to work at a desk near me. She was competent enough
at her job, but Henry wanted her to listen in on my phone calls,
take notes, and pass any questionable information (preferably
'dirt') along to him. Once I saw the situation, I made a deal with
another sub-foreman to exchange Henry's spy with one of his
own employees.

"No doubt, Roy, you'll find more things than you'll need to
know.

"Oh, one last thought. You probably know that Mark Black
and I are not very good friends. I know that he thinks the world
of you for all that you've done for yourself and the Shops. He
and Kettley put trust in you to do the Cost Analysis that we so
sorely need. We didn't get along too well way back when we
were working in the Massachusetts plants. But here, when we
began doing Government jobs, I wanted access to the Bendix job
across the river in Building S-8. But Black wouldn't give us
access, he said, 'for security reasons.' I argued that people in our
Cost Section needed to see the operation, especially the new

machinery in action, etc. But since he had the formal jurisdiction over that part of the Shops, he wouldn't budge, argued about 'Security' although persons like yourself had the necessary passes. Did you ever hear about that issue?"

"No, Al, I can honestly say that I hadn't! But how did it get resolved? I met men like Johnny and Freddie, your Cost men, over there when I was counting drills in the S-8 Tool Crib for Terminations."

"I went to Kettley, who took care of Mark for me! But let me close with another observation before I have to run to another meeting: I was 'kinda' rough on you when we started to talk, downgraded Harvard and the PhD. I both meant it and didn't mean it. I've met a lot of stupid PhD's and MBA's in my time, some who could easily be out-thought and out-maneuvered. I think you've had too much experience as carpenter, mechanic and working here at the Shops to fall into that trap. I don't think that you'll look upon the practical world as many Harvard PhD's do. So I take it back about your leaving S-L-S. I think you'd be crazy to stay because of practical politics and your lack of technical textile knowledge and credentials that employees need in order to rise through the ranks. I've almost 'had it' here and will probably resign soon, too, to save my mind! I hope that part of my legacy will be the notes I'm sharing with you."

He shook hands quite formally. I perused the three note-books for another hour, called Ann Thompson and trudged back to my office where I was greeted by a half dozen picky problems which I disposed of fairly quickly and responded to Grace's and Priscilla's questions of "How did it go?" (They knew how nervous I was about meeting with the Chief Accountant.) I smiled and said, "Remarkably well." As they went off to lunch, I broke out my brown bag and thermos, picked up *The Magic Mountain* and went to our conference room to eat and read.

29. OF APPRENTICES AND EXPERIENCE

One morning when I'd reached the office a little early, I was somewhat surprised by the fact that six or eight of the engineers were gathered in their corner of the room and were engaged in a lively conversation. I couldn't quite catch the drift or topic of the discussion, but I walked past them, took off my sweater to compensate for the stuffiness of the room, tossed my bag lunch into a desk draw, looked up and took a deep breath as John Gold and Fritz Zimmerman strolled to my desk to ask, "May we talk with you a few minutes?"

"Of course, is there a problem?"

"Not really," John replied and went on, "we're a bit puzzled as to why you've not said much about the Saco-Lowell Apprentice Program?"

Fritz chimed in with . . . "From time to time in the past few weeks some of us have met men who've been referred to as 'apprentices,' but none of us have followed up. We've just not had time."

I replied, "I can understand. I remember talking a little about it during our orientation in June, but you'll recall that at that time I was struggling with laryngitis and didn't want to put too much pressure on Grace and Priscilla to do what I should have done or at least followed up."

John broke in, "Look, Roy, we're not complaining, we're

just curious and know that that topic was not a central focus of our work here. And we've gotten pieces of information here, met an occasional apprentice there, but it's something like the six blind persons assembled in order to determine the size and shape of an elephant!"

By this time, most of the engineers had drifted in as well as Grace, Priscilla and Charlie. Evidently, the engineers had decided in advance to call this meeting although I'd had no warning . . . really OK with me.

So I went on, apologizing a little for not having discussed the topic at greater length and depth in June.

GW spoke up, "Enough dancing and BS!" Laughter!

"OK. I think you've raised some good questions. I'm not prepared for a systematic or lengthy story, but I'll do the best I can. Break in any time you wish.

"Well, the Saco-Lowell apprentice program began here in 1930. I recall that date very well because my first awareness of it came when I was a student at Thornton Academy, our high school across the river. I heard about it first hand from a Saco-Lowell machinist who worked on the Tool Making Job and lived near us in Saco. He was one of my dad's favorite persons and talked endlessly about it in dad's garage, explaining why tool-making was so important. Not long after that first lesson, another neighbor shared some of its intricacies; he also worked on the Tool Job, looked my way and said, 'You might be interested, Roy, or at least think about it. After all, you know a lot of about tools since you grew up with them.'

"Not long after that, some of my classmates were talking about what they were going to do after graduation. After all, it was the middle of the Great Depression. Only two of my classmates had families who could afford to send them to college. Another was going on a football scholarship to Catholic University. The two who could afford it were heading for MIT and the University of Maine. Another jokingly remarked, 'As I see it, those of us with no money have three possibilities: the United States Army, the Civil Conservation Corps or Saco-Lowell Tech.' He emphasized the latter disparagingly! As it turned out, I began to think about 'Saco-Lowell Tech,' even though there was a lot of snickering going on in the Thornton hallways when it was called that; I even chastised my classmates with the observation, something to the effect that 'after all, they do have classes in sciences and technology.' As it turned out, I was not among the few who applied to Saco-Lowell, only a couple being admitted.

"Actually one of the prerequisites in the early days included having algebra, geometry and physics. I was a Business major at Thornton, was lucky that I'd had college English and History but had only General Science, no Physics, Chemistry and Calculus. While I might have pushed it and asked for a waiver as some of my classmates did, I decided to gamble and work in my dad's garage. He was always in need of cheap help! When I did by sheer chance get a job here in the Specifications Department, I looked somewhat with awe and envy at several recent TA grads who entered the apprentice program over a number of years; and, as it turned out, when they did graduate, they landed good jobs at the Kittery Navy Yard where some of them, as well as other TA grads, still work, pulling down excellent wages.

"My own perspective was somewhat clouded by the fact that I saw apprentices coming to school on nights when I happened to be working overtime. It was a little upsetting knowing that they were going to classes for which I was ineligible to attend although I had cut circles around them in some of my Thornton courses. I suppose that would surely be called 'envy.' But to be less personal, those who stuck with the classes and practical experience became skilled in Machine Shop Practice and Administration, Drafting Practices & Administration and Foundry Practices & Administration. The apprentices worked forty hours a week, the standard work-week for regular employees. They paid an indenture fee (indentured as in 'indentured servants' from the history of apprentice lore) of fifty dollars which they got back upon successful completion of the program. To my knowledge, no woman was ever admitted, but I'm sure that the Director of the program would share that knowledge.

"This raises a good question; why not bring in the Director of the program or even a graduate, to share his perspective?"

GL broke in. "Hell, Roy, we don't want to become specialists in this topic; we just wanted to get some background." Laughter ensued!

I paused for a moment, raised my hand and asked, "How do the rest of you feel? Want me to try to bring in the Director or a graduate? Or do you agree with George?"

Most put up their hands, but John said, "Maybe there's some way to meet one or two persons, either apprentices or graduates, in the departments where we're working . . . or if not there, in an adjacent department? How would that be?"

A "hear! hear!" rumbled through the group.

I said, "OK, tell you what we'll do. Grace or I will talk with the Director and see if we can get a list of those in the program and learn what department each is in. I may be wrong, but I believe there are some second-hands or sub-foremen who have graduated. I honestly do not know who is who. But I think it's only fair to notify the Shop foremen as well as Superintendents Crosby and Loranger because, as you know, they have some responsibility as to how you use your time on this Cost Project. You are probably tired of hearing us say, 'You are to write history and not spend much time making suggestions for changes in current machining practices and processes.'

"I have one other suggestion. After you get your list and know where the current apprentices or graduates are located, be sure to tell your foreman about your curiosity and give them a rough idea as to how long you'd like to talk with any who fall into this category. Since they, too, have responsibilities, I think that's only fair.

"You have only a few weeks left on this job. We'll try to obtain the list today or tomorrow and have it in your hands before the end of the week. Possibly you'll want to take one or two of the grads to a meal where your discussion can be open-ended. I'd suggest that you avoid turning any meeting into a bitch session; the Union would not like that either. But surely no harm can come from your effort to gain perspective as to why this program gets accolades from all over the country, including Detroit.

"If you wish, let's have a meeting in a couple of weeks so that you may share what you've discovered; in fact, you might have suggestions that can go into your own final reports about your work here. I'm especially interested in your perspectives, in retrospect, about the anti-Semitism and anti-Franco attitudes that some of you encountered. Perhaps too much has already been noised around about these phenomena, but I think that Shops management should have as much data on this phenomenon as they can get . . . although I'll admit some of the management will probably turn a deaf ear to your comments and simply look down their noses and snap, 'From whence it comes!'"

With that, the meeting broke up and I returned to my desk where both Grace and Priscilla were obviously anxious about my view of the meeting. They had listened from the sidelines. I was brief and vague, observed that I thought it was an "OK meeting," then turned to Grace and asked, "Would you please get in touch with the Apprentice Director's secretary to see if you can get a list of both graduates and current enrollees of their program, also where each is currently located, here and in what department or elsewhere? And if possible get a copy today or tomorrow so that we can distribute the list to the engineers by tomorrow when they leave at five; then they'll have the week-end to get their act together to decide what they want to do or maybe learn? Or even forget the whole thing!"

Grace was OK with that, had the lists prepared the next day for the fourteen engineers and handed them out as I'd promised.

Not much was said about the topic during the next two weeks, and I chose not to call a meeting until we were closer to their departure. I hoped that the plan would not lead to any kind of dissension that might become a hurdle to our closing out the Cost Program. From time to time individuals approached me with the information that they'd seen so-and-so from Foundry, Roll Job or whatever. I was careful *not* to get into much detail or open the possibility for dissension that might hurt our project. They continued to discuss their daily collection of blue-prints, lists of parts they were costing; and they seemed at greater ease with Charlie and Lennie as they continued to cost out specific parts with multiple numbers or contradictory infor-mation . . . or sometimes could not fathom hand-writing or machine tool numbers. Fritz Zimmerman's handwriting was especially difficult and Charlie often became sarcastic about their miniscule character, once exclaiming, "Roy, you 'gotta' get us a microscope to deal with Fritz." I sympathized but simply nodded my head.

About a week or two prior to the engineers' scheduled departure, I called a meeting to discuss what they had learned from their interaction with the apprentices and instructors they'd met. In fact, one engineer reported, "I attended two class-es and learned something more about Engineering Administration." All but one engineer had engaged with persons from the Apprentice Program, observing off-hand, "Waste of my time" (in fact, he got up and walked out, mumbling something I could not quite make out, though I think he said, "Damned human-ist!"). Indeed, three of them had taken their apprentices to din-ner. Two were very critical of the S-L-S program, arguing that there was not enough theory of the kind they'd had, one at Carnegie Tech and the other at MIT. One argued that there should be at least one woman in the program. (As he said this, his colleagues gave him a round of "boooooos"! All agreed that the foremen as well as Superintendents Crosby and Loranger, with their assistant, Phil Glaude, had been generous with their time. When I asked how many were willing to put their reac-tions into writing, about half of them raised their hands. And I encouraged them to do so. All but one spoke up to thank me for giving them this opportunity to talk with "the guys," as they continually tagged them.

I concluded with a "Thank you, too, your comments may be an unexpected legacy . . . to go along with your valuable work on the Cost Project . . . especially if we can get relief from the Office of Price Administration!" I came away from the meet-ing with a positive feeling about their contact with the appren-tices they'd met.

As we were breaking up, their leader, Newman, said, "When we're through, I hope that the S-L-S management is suc-cessful with the application for a relief from frozen prices so we can gain some satisfaction from the fact that our efforts have not been in vain. Will you notify us or will your successor do it?"

I assured the group that somebody, possibly Black or Kett-ley, would let them know how we fared in our effort to gain relief . . ."when the news is back from D.C."

30. CHALLENGES & RESPONSES

Following a nightmarish sleep of bad dreams of being chased, clearly related to my encounter with John Morin of Transportation, I awoke angry, hardly spoke with Maryllyn as she drove off to the hospital to sub for a friend on an early shift while I headed for the Shops on my bicycle. I refused to be intimidated by Morin and his gang; and, even as I peddled along, I devised a plan. In fact I was so busy devising, I almost forgot how I had come to work and ended up at the wrong gate. But I was "looking for bear" when I got to the office. Grace and Priscilla saw it in my face and asked, almost in chorus, "What's wrong?"

As gently as possible, I said, "Grace, would you please get a joint appointment with Crosby and Loranger in the same room sometime this morning?" I'd hardly settled down to think about "next steps" when Phil Glaude, Crosby's assistant, had a meeting worked out with the two superintendents, of Saco and Biddeford Divisions. Phil said that they only wanted to know the topic on the table. I said, "Tell them that it's only Transportation!" He called back to say, "Ten o'clock in Crosby's office." I liked that because it saved me from "legging" the longer distance to Saco.

While Grace and Priscilla watched me like the proverbial mother hens and brought me coffee, I planned my speech to the two superintendents, deciding *not* to threaten but rather to per-

202

suade! I left the office a little early in order to pace off two or three areas where Transportation's tractors had nearly run me down. I knew I needed to be exact. When I arrived at Crosby's office, both he and Loranger were discussing a boxing problem involving one of our best customers of repair parts; this involved a part of Saco-Lowell not closed by the war.

I said hello to Phil and addressed each as "Mister," and they invited me to sit down, asking if I'd like coffee.

"No thanks," I replied, "I'm already hyped enough!"

"So what's the problem?" they both asked almost in unison. Then Crosby added, "Should we ask Phil to listen in case we need his stenographic skills?"

I assured them that it was "OK with me," so they summoned him to join us and take a back seat.

I began by saying how angry I had been since nearly being run down by one of the electric tractors near the Biddeford Erecting room. I described the situation, even citing the approximate inches via which I'd been missed; then, I cited the fact that I'd also been nearly hit in the yard when the driver swung his machine fifteen or twenty feet out of his way to threaten my safety, probably to scare me. I went on to describe what had happened in John Morin's office when I went in to see him to try to find out what was happening, even asking . . . "was I a marked man or on a contract?" I then cited instances where others had been threatened. I added, "And, of course, you're familiar with the death of Harold Hendy, killed by one of our trucks on the ramp entering the Saco building."

Both men nodded in acknowledgement. So I went on: "How many accidents has our First Aid Room reported in the past five years, as Johnny Morin's electric tractor jockeys play chicken in our narrow aisles or even in the Foundry while they're pouring hot metals? Who's reported what?"

As I ended my diatribe, both men wore sober expressions, and Jim Crosby looked at Phil as though to ask whether he had anything to report. Phil responded, "I've heard about close calls, and I believe that a couple of accidents were reported to First Aid a year or so ago. Other than that . . . ?" He shrugged as if to say, "That's it!"

Then Crosby spoke, "I know that Johnny's quite a tractor jockey . . . but we can't fault him for the fact that he delivers materials on schedule, department to department, shop to shop, Saco to Biddeford and vice versa. We've heard of many misses since he became head of Transportation about five years ago. Yet, we've never taken the time to check First Aid or poll the shops' foremen to learn if there have been accidents or near accidents that never got tallied. Roy, we probably can't reveal all that we know because of union restraints and personnel secrecy files. But . . ."

And I spoke up, "But Mr. Crosby, does somebody else have to get killed before we put speed regulators on the tractors? Or install better horns on them? Or even fine drivers a week's pay when we learn of a 'near miss' and have a hearing to check its veracity? It is my guess that the drivers operate their machines within the limits of threats so long as the tractors' cargoes deliver, deliver, deliver! I can remember eight years ago when I came to work for SLS, I encountered a weird indifference to the rights of 'pedestrians' trying to get place to place in the shops. There must be some way to demand some kind of safety for those of us who have little defense from having merely the status of 'helpless pedestrians.' Have the two or three of you [looking toward Phil] ever been threatened?"

At that point Loranger asserted, "The laissez-faire attitude that we have taken in the name of 'production' may have been irresponsible? I've been nearly hit myself, but when I've heard the tractors coming, I've usually stopped, stepped aside and found a safe haven behind a post or between a couple of machines, whatever was handiest. I think that Roy's right and that we should take steps, put up 'caution' signs, interrogate the drivers. After all, there aren't too many of them. I think that we need to bring in Johnny to hear what he has to say for or about himself and department. Nor do I think that we need to expose anybody who protests the behavior of that department. As Roy has suggested, it would be fairly easy to 'mark' an unpopular guy or one who was perceived as dangerous to his occupation!" He looked across the room at Phil who continued to scribble with deliberation, asked, "What do you think?"

Phil took a deep breath, straightened up in his chair, then observed, "I don't think that Roy's on the side of the angels, he never has been! (laughter!) But I doubt if he'd come in here to discuss the matter if he didn't mean it. I've known him most of his life; we went to school together. He usually says what he thinks, regardless of consequences!"

A pause came over the office, then Crosby asked Phil if he'd taken any notes from the meeting.

Phil nodded. Then Jim said, "I think we must be cautious in how we take our next steps, how we collect and how we use what information we get. I believe that most of the employees in that department belong to the Union. Also, should this meeting become public information, Roy's life might not be worth a dime! What say we get Phil to write up the meeting; let us all read it, meet again or discuss it on the phone after we've had time to sleep on it (and Roy I hope you can sleep!). Let's all think about it, make some more inquiries, then get on the phone to decide where we are and/or what action to take. And, Roy, I'm sorry about the danger you've encountered and for your loss of sleep (he chuckled). You may have saved somebody's life or lives?"

As he dismissed the meeting, Loranger shook my hand, looked me square in the face said quietly, "Many thanks."

I shook Phil's hand, gave him a pat on the shoulder and strolled slowly back to the office, wishing I had eyes in the back of my head as well as in front!

31. DESIGN; APPEARANCE; FUNCTION

It was noon. The office was empty. I was just starting lunch and the last chapter of *The Magic Mountain* when the phone rang.

"Hello?"

"Gordon Anderson, from Research and Development calling. Roy, let's finish that conversation/interview that we started the other day? I'm having a snack. Bring yours down and we can talk and eat together."

"Great! I'll be right there!"

As I walked into his modernized office/work room, I was especially impressed by the neon ceiling lights and commented, "Hi, Gordon, no wonder you can shed light on the engineering and design processes."

"Nobody can have fun with puns more than you!"

"Thanks, Gordon, most folk don't catch the spirit of that mental exercise!"

But I immediately added, "As I recall, you'd given me some background about your family. Your mom hailed from Nova Scotia and your father was 'sort of a home-grown philosopher.' Said he liked to sit back and reflect about things. You also said that as an adult you became aware that he had put together what you called, 'a sense of values and a philosophy of life' that would do honor to more-educated people, especially his attitude toward work as a great disciplinarian. He was somewhat like my dad and the way he looked at work. Do you want to continue from there?"

"Sure, that's a good place to start on the more technical stuff. Yeah, I don't know that I fully realized the importance of that, but I eventually said to myself, 'By golly, for a guy with no education, he had things lined up pretty well.' As a kid I was somewhat of an introvert so I had a great curiosity. I took apart more alarm clocks and all that stuff than anybody I knew. I remember that somebody once gave me a one-tube radio which I took apart but couldn't re-assemble!"

"A crystal set?"

"Something like that, I think! But let's get to where I came into the textile industry and design! I began to think more about textile processes than the machinery . . ."

"But, Gordon," I asked, "how do you distinguish between the two? Don't you need the machine in order to have the process?"

"Yeah, Roy, but let's take long-draft spinning where the object is to utilize as many lengths of fiber as possible. Basically, that's a process, but there are a hundred ways you could design a machine to do the job."

"But, didn't most mills keep retain their basic machines and apply 'changeover parts' only what was above the beam; namely the rolls and their supporting mechanisms?

"Yeah! So to test the new ideas, we developed a big yarn lab up there where your office is now and we did a lot of testing, but seemed uninterested in improving the mechanical design of the equipment. And this is where my views of design came in so let me say a word or two about that. As I see it, there are three major objectives in designing machinery for the capital goods market. First is functional performance. If the machine doesn't do something new or something old, or faster, or cheaper, you know, there's no point in pursuing its modification. Cost is the second big objective. The cost has to be justified by the performance, and it has to be probable that the manufacturer of the machine can make a profit just as the customer can, too. Third, appeal or 'appearance' are important."

"Cosmetics, as it were?"

"You got it, Roy!"

"Some of our customers may say that as long as it works and they can afford it, that's enough! But if you grow up in the design business, as I did, you become aware that most people do put more stock in good appearance than they know because intuitively they associate good performance with good appearance. Also this ties to ergonomics because people like to be comfortable when they're working on a machine, that it's built to fit people . . . so it's easy to operate and they can enjoy it."

"Gordon, let me respond to that word, 'ergonomics,' it's rather a new one for me, but isn't it really a matter of human adaptation to a machine? Are we on the same page? And have all three of these qualities been operational here at Saco-Lowell?"

"Yes, but everybody may not have been too aware of it. Sometimes it's easy to get lost by working too damned hard on one of these factors that they lose track of the others. But before we get lost in other minutia related to appeal, let me speak of Virgie Burnham, probably one of the most creative of all designers employed here at the Shops. After he changed the way top rolls are held down, using magnetism, some designers asked, 'Why didn't I think of that?' For years, the top rolls were held against the bottom rolls (to put the pressure on the thread), held down by saddles and stirrups. You probably know that?"

'Yes!"

"Well, Virgie asked, 'Gee wouldn't it be nice if we just dropped a big magnet on the top rolls?' So we did that and it worked because we didn't need a weighting mechanism with its accompanying worry about bearings wearing out. You can run the steel rolls in plastic bearings to save both money and worry. And technically speaking, the magnetic force decreases inversely as the square of the distance between the two poles."

"Isn't that *change* what's becoming known as 'Magnadraft'?"

"Yes, Roy, at least tentatively and that was a good 'sticker' for PR and sales!"

"Gordon, do you want to add to the three concepts that you just outlined for me?"

"I don't think I was aware of them when I came to work here. I was just a young designer in my early years here, and it seemed to me that Saco-Lowell was focused on performance before appearance; but I think that the decline of sales was one of the things that turned their perspectives around; after all, President Edwards and VP Kettley were tired of heading a losing corporation, that is, one in the red! I don't know how many millions they were in the hole after consolidating the three mills. Also do you know the story of moving from the use of cast iron for the large head ends on machines to steel not long before the war?"

"Yes, but not from a design perspective."

"Well, we had to take a different view. We knew that the Foundry processes were very labor intensive. At first it seemed like a 'no-no' because of the high cost of machine tools involving a shift from cast iron to steel. It was well known that investment for the new technology if we shifted to steel, where costs were major . . . that we'd need to use stampings, selected aluminum extrusions, plastic, etc. that eventually became incorporated into the textile machines. But that's the direction we went. I think it was Virgie Burnham's influence that led to hiring Tom Kerry.

"Who was?"

"Tom Kerry was an industrial designer who knew practically nothing about textile machinery, but he knew what color it ought to be, what decorations it should have as well as the different bulks in the machine, you know the things that would please people. His input led to changes in the machines' appearances. You can see it for yourself if you look at a range of catalogues beginning in the Twenties then advance your search year by year although the major shifts happened relatively recently.

"I feel fortunate to have been here during the evolution of this revolution. That's a personal feeling and I don't know how many others feel that way. I realize that you have to make compromises, the best ones between function, cost and appearance. I used to lecture my design engineers, probably ad nauseam, 'It's 'gotta' work! It's 'gotta' work!'"

"Gordon, do you want to say more about your specific role in this textiles revolution?"

"Well, there were lots of changes. The so-called old guard, under people like Blake and Northway (of automobile-manu-facturing fame and early influence on Henry Ford), disappeared and new blood was brought in. Sometimes it was hard to take, and I was once tempted to leave Saco-Lowell and move to two other textile machine manufacturers. But I saw that the grass was *not* greener in Southern New England so I stuck it out here and I'm glad because I especially enjoyed working with Research Chief, Bob Jones and Virge."

Looking at my watch I said, "I've got two more questions as well as a one o'clock appointment back at my office. My questions about Virge relate to the times in my pre-Bates days when we walked to work together because we lived in the same Saco neighborhood. I knew Bob Jones only slightly because our paths rarely crossed here in the office area. How would you distinguish between the two men? I saw the more practical side of Virge, who was always working on Classical American furnishings or some other gadget at home or with friends like Laurence Dolby. But at the design end, was he a kind of intuitive soul who would, understandably find the simplicity of magnetism; would that insight characterize him? Did he see the beauty of simplicity? About Jones: was he more of an administrator? Did he have any patents? Wasn't he associated with improving the roving machine?"

"Roy, let me say that your characterization of the key guys in this department is 'right on'; good comparisons. As for the patents on the roving machine, I hold them!"

"Wow! Excuse me for *that* faux pas, Gordon! Maybe it's a good time for me to ask my last question and leave! Since I first stepped foot into this company, as a kid just out of high school, I have noted an increased number of orders from overseas in places like Russia and South America. It may be simplistic to ask: wouldn't the newly-built mills, installing the most newly-designed machines, have a competitive advantage on the world's textile market? At least that seems logical to me."

Gordon stopped and rubbed his chin a moment, then observed, "I've heard some of our salesmen use that pitch, but I really don't know how far they may have carried the research or design-driven argument. You know, Roy, I think that might be a good question to take to our next Design Group discussions where we've been looking at some of the more advanced applications of technology. Perhaps talk with Sales, too? I'm predicting that in a decade or two from 1944 we'll be using electronics, even though that field is now in its infancy. But I'll carry your question to our group as early as next week. Thanks for suggesting it, Roy."

Glancing at his watch, he said, "You'd better run! Duty calls us both! Feel free to come back or quote anything I've said. I hope you've taken good notes."

"Thanks, Gordon." And I hastened back to the office where I found Grace and Priscilla talking with my one o'clock visitor.

32. HALL OF HEROES

A day or two after my interview with Gordon, I got a call out of the blue from Kettley's Secretary, Lawrence Perry, who announced that there was a reception for President Edwards in the Conference Room and adjacent hallways that afternoon, to honor some of the important men (with no women mentioned) in the history of the corporation. Ed Henry, Larry's immediate boss had relayed the word from Kettley, which surprised me. I'd said hello to Henry many times, especially when I revised his copies of Specifications and Parts Lists eight years ago. But I was never quite clear how he used copies of those documents nor what his role was in the Shops hierarchy. Anyway, Larry's question was succinct: "Can you attend? It probably won't last more than an hour to ninety minutes?"

Busy as I was trying to wrap up the Cost Job or leave it in appropriate shape for my already chosen successor, I knew what this was not an invitation but a command. So I said, "Yes, but I have no appropriate attire here on site for such an occasion."

Larry said, "Don't worry. I have a spare suit coat and tie. Come down through the back door of my office. You can put them on in my back-room 'closet toilet.'"

I said, "OK, but tell me something, Larry, what's Ed Henry got to do with the price of bananas in this company?"

"Oh, he has a wealthy wife who's both loaned and given money to the company. Except for a secretary or two, she may be the only woman at the afternoon affair. Between you and me, Ed's nothing but an 'old busybody,' aptly named by those in the know (the Chief Accountant had tipped me off). Simply be polite and don't raise any controversial issues. In other words, just bow and scrape and enjoy the refreshments!"

"Larry, you know I don't 'bow and scrape' easily!"

Larry laughed, signed off, "See you this afternoon."

When Grace and Priscilla turned in unison, curious as to "what that was all about," I informed them, concluding with a query and a chuckle, "Do you want to upset the apple cart and come with me?"

They replied chorus-like, "No way!" I smiled, figuring I could do a few desk jobs since going into the shops for some of my farewells would have to wait a day or two longer. So I thumbed through some of the cost sheets to see if I could answer some of the questions that others in the office had targeted for me. Meanwhile I was grinding my brain with Larry's info about Ed Henry. My major question: "Why hadn't I run into that scuttlebutt before?"

The hour of charm arrived at mid-afternoon and I took Larry's advice by entering the entertainment area via his back door. Larry's extra suit coat and tie didn't quite fit me, but I took a quick look in the bathroom mirror, exclaimed to myself, "What th' 'ell!" and joined Larry as he eased into what was becoming a large and loud crowded room. I recognized the two superintendents, and some of the more prominent foremen and designers; also I spied Phil Glaude, my old Thornton Academy schoolmate, and the superintendents' assistant, made a bee-line for him, shook hands, asked, "What's this all about?"

Phil responded, "Two things on the agenda: one is the

unveiling of some of the pictures of prominent figures in our corporate history, agents, former presidents or whatever they were called. Then, too, Kettley and Black will introduce David Edwards and Mrs. Henry. They've been planning this for some time and I was asked to do research for the dates, all six of them to be exact, plus Edwards and Kettley. All you have to do is LOOK interested, Roy, but don't open your damned mouth!"

Phil had known me since grade school, hence his warning was on target. Well, I circulated among some of the people I knew, shaking hands and indulging in small talk, answering questions about progress with the Cost Project. In each instance, I was succinct, "OK, it's coming along fine." A couple of draftsmen wished me luck in grad school. The word had gotten around.

Finally at the appointed hour, Mark Black came through the main entrance and mimicked the Announcer of the President of the United States when entering the Chambers of Congress. Mark nearly made the announcement a mockery in saying, "Ladies and Gentlemen, the President of the U . . . I mean Saco-Lowell." Edwards was so close behind him that Black nearly lost his heels. Edwards stepped onto the small raised platform, built for the occasion, turned to face the standing audience and quickly said, "and I have the privilege of introducing Mrs. Amanda Henry, a member of the S-L-S's Corporation Board and an important benefactor of this great company. Without her financial skills and timely loans we'd never have survived." With that introduction, a smiling Mrs. Henry stepped to Edwards' side. No effort whatever was made to ask Ed Henry to join them.

I quickly ran Lawrence Perry's words through my mind. No wonder he served S-L-S as Busybody emeritus!

But our attention soon turned to Kettley who had joined

Edwards and Henry on the platform. Black, teetering a bit at the edge of the platform, almost fell off, smiled a bit, then held on, grasping a scroll in his right hand. Edwards rather quickly moved the meeting along with the remark, "Mr. Kettley is CEO of this plant so I wish to honor him by honoring others." Kettley appeared to be very nervous and passed the baton to Black, almost physically. Since Black was holding one scroll already and was not prepared to accept another; again he almost fell off the platform. In fact a few persons standing close by made a move to grab him so he'd not fall off. Black, usually a man of poise, was visibly embarrassed, but caught himself, with an assist from Kettley and began unrolling the scroll as he started to speak.

"Lady and gentlemen, I am honored to read the names and dates of six men of this corporation without whose efforts we probably would not be here. We could probably find at this very moment ten times these numbers, possibly ten times ten; and, indeed, we promise to expand this gallery of heroes annually."

With this comment Ed Henry advanced to the veiled pictures, each 12" x 18" in size. And as Ed pulled the veil from each, Mark Black merely recited the person's name and dates; namely, Samuel Bachelder, Otis Pettee, E.E. Blake, James McMullan, Frank J. Hale and Robert F. Herrick. I had met Blake during my first days at Saco-Lowell, others were lost in the mists of cotton lint and history. But I could never have guessed what was coming next!

After repeating the names and pictures of the six men, now staring at one another with at least one scowling as if to say, "Why this?" Ed gave Mark a signal and invited the group to look toward the podium where David Edwards had unveiled Kettley's and his own portraits simultaneously. Both men appeared to be stunned, then Amanda Henry began to speak.

216

"We expected no woman would join this heroic group; after all, we've just been given the vote!"

For this remark, the audience rewarded her with a spontaneous applause.

Mrs. Henry paused for a few moments, observing, "Maybe we'll have a woman represented by the Year 2000."

More applause and cheering with a few "boos" around the fringes. She continued with her speech, "Maybe I shouldn't have said that?" to which more screaming of "*no*'s" after which she continued. "In all seriousness, I don't feel badly that no women are represented here; in light of what's coming, the tasks ahead will be more fun. I can say truly that I've enjoyed my part in Saco-Lowell's life because there were times we thought it might die. I thank both Mr. Edwards and Mr. Kettley for their vision and their hard work. I know many others who should be honored and maybe their time will come. At the risk of offending others, I want to say how much I appreciate the progress the apprentice program has made . . . as well as that of the designers and re-designers and I believe there's emerging a generation of re-re-designers (and she pointed to Virgie Burnham)." There was a brief applause for Virgie as I caught Gordon Anderson's eye for just a moment and he lifted his eyebrows. Mrs. Henry continued, "I hope that Messrs Black and Kettley are successful with their Special Cost Project; and, looking down the highway to the future, I hope that we get the Government to thaw frozen prices" (both Kettley and Black gave me the nod . . . which was not missed by people like Chief Accountant, Al Stuart, who detested Mark's guts; I witnessed that feeling via his scowl).

But now Mrs. Henry, show person that she was, reached into a box her attendant opened for her and pulled out a white rabbit and held it over her head! She looked around the room that had burst into laughter and paused to enjoy the entire effect. As the room became quiet, she cradled the rabbit in her bare arms and began speaking again. "You'll note that we did not identify the photos by write-up, nor do we intend to do so on this occasion. Rather, we have a surprise that may be as unexpected as the rabbit." She paused and somebody from the rear of the room shouted, "Are you going to turn the rabbit into a new-model carding machine?" More laughter.

"No I am announcing a contest. We want you to do the research for the identity and contributions of the six men in the pictures we've unveiled today. Mostly, they come from different generations than we know. We want you to identify them and make clear in no more than 100 words what their place is in the history of Saco-Lowell. I know that that will not be easy because we gave Phil Glaude the task of finding the birth and death dates of these men and it was not easy to find data! My photo is not here yet, but I'll never reveal when I was born or intend to die!" More laughter.

"We are offering a financial incentive of a week's pay for the ones who develop the best inscriptions to be placed on brass plates beside the photos. I know that those of you who feel underpaid may feel that a week's pay is not enough." A rippled effect rolled through the crowd!

"But we offer another incentive. Not only will your name or names be attached to each photo, but you will have the honor of making a presentation of your inscription or inscriptions next year when we have the Second Annual Day of Heroes, a day such as this. We hope that many of you will feel honored to enter the contest, even though we don't expect you to do your research while on the job (more laughter and boo's), but we also hope you'll enter a second contest; namely, of writing a more dangerous kind of inscription to be added to the photos of Messrs Edwards and Kettley at next year's event. I say 'dangerous' because an unappreciative commentary, no matter how many words, might be subject to disciplinary action."

A voice from the back: "Where's Saco-Lowell Siberia?"

Mrs. Henry was up to responding to the caustic question, reacting, "Wherever, it's surrounded by cold roll steel, 1020!"

With that remark, Edwards broke in with another announcement. "There may be another incentive, too; Harvard Business School is working on a history of Saco-Lowell, hence your photo captions may become part of our legacy when the author, George Gibb, finishes his research and writing. This is an invitation to contact him, but no harassment, please."

Mrs. Henry had the last word, thanking the group for their attention and contributions to the levity of the occasion; then, declared the meeting adjourned in the "spirits of which there are many (over there in the next room) . . . after which, don't go back to work! There's no knowing what kind of machinery you'll produce if you do; simply put it off until Monday!" This brought a roar of approval and more applause. After a little wine, I knew my bicycle was close, so I took her seriously!

33. FOND, FONDER & FONDEST FAREWELLS

Down through the last week of my tenure at Saco-Lowell, I had gradually released all but one of the imported engineers, working in the Small Parts Department in the Saco Plant, attended a farewell dinner which the leader of the visiting engineering sponsored. While I never detected much interaction of this diverse group with their various experiences and parts of the country, they seemed like old buddies of yore at this occasion. I was pleased that they invited the entire office group. They gave me a collective cheer and a semi-roast when their leader permitted only "a few words to a speech but less than a sentence" about anybody:

"more protester than Protestant"

"too humanistic to survive the corporate world"

"more fair than Fairfield"

"too enmeshed in the gears of history"

The very next engineer, well known for his fondness of rhyming and couplets remarked, "needing more info re: mystery of history!"

Laughter! And I had Grace present to record the exact words of each person and any important dates we should remember. Others went on:

"Does Charley scratch his name into the Yankee line-up ev'ry day?" (more laughter and Charley's face turns red)?"

". . . Roy's ancestor a king, 'roi'?" (to which I responded, "my grandmother was; her 42nd cousin was the first governor of Maine, William King!")

". . . parts sheets drove me to an ophthalmologist; thank you, Priscilla" (She stood up and did a neat little curtsy) (another round of applause).

". . . the clown of the group, also a punster: ". . . to Grace who needs little more grace than she already has." She, too, stood up and copied Priscilla's curtsy.

Down to this point "GL" had remained silent. Now he stood up, banged his glass with a spoon for quiet and began a kind of valedictory, remarking: "Roy, all of this is great fun, surely more than some days rewarded us (not counting our salaries). But in all seriousness, you were a very human director of this program. You understood our various backgrounds, you resolved some serious personal conflicts; you have an incredible ability to see the 'other guy's' viewpoint. We salute your intelligence and humanity. I regret that I shall never be your student sometime in the future somewhere in a university setting. I think you'll make a unique college 'prof' because I think you'll hear your students better than most college 'profs do."

He then reached down behind his chair and lifted a plaque and a glass bowl onto the table, unwrapped each separately, then read:

To Roy Fairfield, Director of Special Cost Project for Saco-Lowell Shops, in the spirit of the engineering profession and academia, we grant you an honorary Doctorate in Engineering Humanism. We commend you for being the best of Maineacs we've met and come to know.

Signed, George L. Spielman
June–October, 1944

This statement was followed by the names and signatures of the fourteen members of the engineering team.

Since I was expected to say something in response to their shouting "speech, speech" and their applause, I got to my feet, feeling glad that the group numbered only 25 or 30. Actually I felt week in the knees and leaned on a chair.

I began, "Thank you for your brevity and levity if not entirely your 'honesty.' I truly didn't think we had it in us to do what we've done in the past four or five months. When you arrived, you'll recall that I was practically speechless. Possibly my laryngitis was triggered by fear because I'd never associated so closely with so many engineers in my life. With only a few minor incidents, I thought we got along famously. You caught the notion of the Saco Lowell mission, much of which was and still is, related to survival. I think that Fred Cote, over there in the corner [and I now introduce him for a round of applause] will integrate our efforts in order to support our appeal to the Office of Price Administration for post-war pricing relief.

"I appreciate the levity of this occasion and hope that I'll live up to 'GL's expression of confidence in me as a potentially humane professor or at least in the humanistic tradition. I hope that I can use some of my better Bates professors as role models; and, if I can't have you as my students, perhaps some of your children will enroll wherever I happen to be. My good thoughts and a 'Bon Voyage' for your trips wherever you are going. This has been an important learning experience for me despite some of my continuing political and engineering naivete."

We continued friendly handshakes and words around the restaurant table. I was especially pleased to see the engineers mixing with the office workers who had tried so hard to assist them while working for the Saco-Lowell Shops. I returned home to relate the story and was sorry that Maryllyn chose not to attend.

The next morning, my next to last on the project, found me working closely with Grace, Priscilla and Fred Cote to be sure that we'd covered all the bases, dotted the "I's" and crossed the "T's.". Fred had talked with Kettley and Black to be sure there would be no slippage as I phased out and he phased in. We agreed that Priscilla and Grace would continue to do their specific jobs, Grace to handle the coordination and Priscilla to hang close to needs for redoing some of the cost sheets that were not clear and would need Shop assistance. We also agreed to keep Charlie for another week at the Frieden calculator and an occasional trip to the shops; this would give him time to transfer to the job he'd obtained in a power station up-river, one that met his need for more exercise than the one he'd worked all summer.

Fred had scanned a large percentage of our engineering-prepared sheets, found a few glitches but in general felt that the project could be wrapped up in a reasonable amount of time. He commended us for what we had done to complete in six or seven months what his home-base, the Cost Department, had predicted would require five years. Also, he knew that both of my supervisors, Black and Kettley, as well as the department foremen and two superintendents were pleased with our production.

I agreed to work that afternoon with Grace, Priscilla and Fred on details and obvious gaps; also, I had some routine thank-you notes to write so Grace would help me by taking dictation. Priscilla agreed to proof and retype the twenty-plus page formal report that I was writing to Black as a kind of finish to my part in the project. All of this planning left me free to spend my last day, circulating in the office and shops to thank special persons and say "So long" to persons, some of whom I'd known for more than eight years. Such a last-moment visit was certainly *not* required, rather it was something I wanted to do.

My last Friday: Late October, 1944
I'd planned the route of my trip through the offices and shops fairly carefully and decided to visit my oldest friends in the Specs & List Office first. I recalled that they'd given me a Farewell Party, with lots of going-away gifts, when I'd left for Bates College in September 1939. But most of them were aware that I was taking an even higher risk seeking my doctorate at Harvard; yet, they were prepared again to say "good-bye." Since my home base was still in Saco and Biddeford, I would, of course, try to visit on vacations. But in some sense these were emotional moments since some of them were "up there" in age. Others such as Perce Harper and Evy Beaupreau had already died; Sandy Parker married a high school classmate and left the area. But I had a good laugh or two that Mac McGinness continued to spar with Mark Black via prize roses which the two matched with one another, summer to summer, to be informally awarded as *"best."*

During my tour I learned, too, that Harry Scamman, one of Maryllyn's cousins, continued to bring bushels of fresh yellow corn to office mates and had only recently brought in the last ears of the season. Too, Ralph Perry, my old friend of many years, continued to play practical jokes on Dick Prince, the Biddeford shop foreman of Shipping; but we agreed that nothing that he had done recently began to match our feat of sending him the sow's ear challenging him to make a silk purse from it.

Our mutual jokester friend, Brownie Duke gave me a farewell hug, and I thanked him again for having started me out right in my approach to changing shop specs when I came to work, especially in my approach to relating carefully to shop foremen and second hands. We also discussed what was once a forbidden topic, that is, his unfortunate experience of losing a testicle in one of the Central American "revolutions." I also learned that Jim Lawshaw and Ethel Bravard were still dating; I kidded them for setting the world's longest engagement record at 28 years . . . or if not Guinness's, then New England's; they laughed but would not give me a date for their wedding! They still told me that they loved me and wished me well in Cambridge.

While talking with those in the Spec's office, I could see Mark Black through the window that divided their office from his. He seemed to be holding a session with a committee, so I decided to move on to the Drafting Room to say "Good-bye" to old friends some of whom I'd also known since I came to work in the shops. Most of them were working at their boards so I simply went down the room speaking to each in turn.

"Hi neighbor," I addressed Harry Rivers. After all, he lived just across the Portland Road from my boyhood home. "This is my last day, Harry, so I just stopped by to shake hands and thank you again for accepting me to the Saco & Biddeford camera group some years ago. I didn't do too well in your contests, but you and your senior friends such as George Lovenstein gave me some helpful tips. As always, Harry was congenial and wished me well, adding, "If you do as well at Harvard as you did in living up to Marian's recommendation when you applied to Bates, you'll do OK." I thanked him and moved on to Harry Rhodes's board.

Harry greeted me warmly. "Harry, I have many good memories of our time together a couple of years ago when we were tooling up for the Ford bogey wheel job; but, the one thing I shall always remember you for is how you made the arrow sign on your drawings by cutting off one "leg" of the arrow and sharpening the point by sizing down the other "leg" until it hugged the long part of the arrow. In fact, I know of nobody else in this drafting room or any other place where I see maps or measurements to indicate distances from point to point where it's used. I may have asked you this before, but have you ever tried to get it patented?

Harry looked up quizzically from his drafting board, still "nursing" his stubborn corncob pipe, remarked, "No, and I doubt if it could be; after all, it's part of the tools we use in making drawings and hence prints. Do you really think it could be patented?"

"I really don't know, Harry, but no harm trying!" I left him scratching his head while trying to get his neighbor, Dick Street's attention. Just as Dick turned to respond to Harry, I entered his space and smiled and pondered over the direction that my query about the arrow might take. I paused a moment, then stepped between the two men. "Just dropped by to say 'So long,' Dick, I'm off to see if I can earn a Post-hole-Digger in the big time. But before I left I wanted you to know how good it's been knowing the father of a couple of my favorite people at Thornton, your sons Don and John. As you probably remember, I taped their ankles for their years on the TA football team."

"Yeah, I remember you from that time. I once stepped into the training room just before a game, saw you ripping tape with your bare hands, was impressed. Of course, both boys kept me informed. But I hope the PhD will be more than a joke for you."

"Just kidding, Dick, I'll probably be so exhausted and disgusted with the graduate system I may want to disown it. Thanks for the nudge."

I then saw Charlie Harkness coming from the rest room area so I followed him to his drafting board. I'd never been too friendly with Charlie since I felt a bit guilty for having left his Boy Scout troop at age 13 without saying "Good-bye," hence did not rise to the challenge he presented. As I recalled, I'd not even earned a Second-class rank, let alone Eagle, the highest rank in scouting. But anyway, I shook hands, thanked him for having inspired me three or four years before, especially when I heard him demonstrating his skill as organist at my home-town church. Also, I marveled how he could teach "Mechanical Drawing" nights and still fill a full-time slot here.

"Thanks, Roy. I do remember your time in the Scouts, enjoyed our trips to Kennebunk Pond and Acton Fair Grounds, hoped you'd become an Eagle Scout, you seemed to have a broad talent, both intellectually and physically, and never did know why you dropped out."

That put me on the spot, so I felt compelled to say nothing, about not liking his womanizing. I simply said, "It was a family matter and my dad needed help in the garage." This was a half truth because dad did use me in his business, especially Saturdays and nights when he had emergency calls from his regular customers.

I went to see my next draftsman friend, feeling a little guilty for the half-fib, but needing to push on. "Hi, George, just saw your photography comrade, Harry, up there at the head of your table line. I have always appreciated what you tried to teach me, but I didn't make it and have felt a little chagrined about my failures. But I think that I was intimidated by your photographic equipment and ability to construct and use a dark room. As you know, that was beyond my pocketbook."

"Harry and I fully understood and know that you did as well as you could. But as you say, 'Good-bye' to Saco-Lowell, at least for the moment, I have been meaning to commend you for learning the file and contract numbers in the Spec's Dept. You must have saved hundreds, maybe thousands of hours giving us numbers off the top of your head and saving Drafting, Engineering and Repair Parts Department members from seeking them from the card catalogue. How did you do it?"

"I don't know, George; when I saw that I could save much time in my filing job, sitting there beside the master files, I simply learned them as a function of my job as well as expediting the work for others. I didn't take it on because I was told to do so; I thought of it as a 'tool' we could all use."

"Well we used it all right!"

"Thanks, George, but one other point of our contact. You'll recall that a year or so ago I was doing genealogical work in my spare time at Dyer Library. And you helped me with one branch of my family because your own spliced with mine a couple of centuries ago. I appreciated your taking time with me. My grandmother did, too, because she wasn't aware of that branch of the King family until you helped us."

Next, I crossed the drafting room to those working on another division of textile machines, Mill Layouts. Some of the desks were empty, because the guys were at a meeting with the master designer of the old Kitson equipment. But Earle Rich and Willis John were there, so I dropped by and stood between their drafting boards. "Thank you both for answering questions about mill lay-outs when I needed them over the years."

They both smiled appreciatively just as Ike Roberts, having just punched the nearby time clock rolled in, almost literally, with a big smile and "Hi!" for the three of us.

"Tough night, Ike?"

"Yeah our band got stuck in Augusta after the concert, at 3:30 AM, no gasoline, no way to get home with all our instruments, too late to call families . . . so we shacked up in an old beaten-up hotel, had permission from Irv [the chief of drafting] to check in late if we ran into such a situation. Anyway, what's cookin'? Roy, I hear you're goin' back ta school?"

"Yep, this is my last day so I just dropped by to thank a few folk for helping me in various ways. I add thanks to you, Earle and Willis, for your insights about mill lay-outs. But I have another debt to repay you, Ike."

Ike frowned, squinting up his face then asked, "What are you talking about? You don't owe me anything!"

"Not true, Ike. Do you remember the times that you climbed up on the blueprint files in the vault, impersonated a monkey, scratched your chest as monkeys sometimes do and had us all in stitches or wetting our pants as we egged you on with peanuts, sometimes literally until the Keeper of the Blue-prints gave us hell for messing up the place. Do you remember? You did it for a whole month of lunches. I'm nearly wetting my pants laughing, just remembering the details!"

Earle piped up, "I remember because Black and El Giles got together and laid down the law, threatening to send us *all* the cleaning bill."

An older and more conservative Willis, said soberly, "I remember, too!"

By this time we were all laughing hilariously because Ike had hopped up on his tall drafting table stool and was starting to repeat his act. Some of those from across the room, sensing another show, tip-toed over and peeked out from behind a row of filing cabinets which tended to divide the huge room. Ike acted out the showman that he was, this time moving from being a monkey to being a banjo player and the bandleader that he was to being *Just Plain Ike* whom I would remember all the days of my life. But, it was a fitting way to say, "Good-bye" to friends who were not close, but who treated me as a mature adult even when I was but 18. Again, I shook hands all around even as El and Black moved quietly down the drafting room to check on what was happening.

Checking my watch and seeing that it was nearly noon, I returned to the Cost Project office to see if all was OK and to clean out my desk to prepare to take home what few of my possessions were still there, especially my well-marked up copy of Thomas Mann's *The Magic Mountain*. And since Grace and Priscilla were eating their lunches in the Conference Room, I stepped in to eat my last lunch with them. Neither was particularly talkative, but they asked about moving to Arlington, Massachusetts and what that life might be for Maryllyn and me with a two-year old daughter. Although I felt especially shaky about what the future might hold, I told them about the German entry exam I had to take and for which I had been prepping, "in my spare time'" all summer. As best I could, I told them what I knew about the four courses for which I had signed up, tentatively. Also, I invited them to come see us if they got to the Boston area. I shared with them some of my worries; namely, unknowns about finance, the nature of the neighborhood we were moving into, the skimpily furnished apartment, the prospects and strains of commuting by bus the five miles from Arlington Heights to Harvard Square.

Both Grace and Priscilla were empathetic, saying that they might not have the courage to do it with all the unknowns; yet, Priscilla said that she had grown up with me, seen my work at Saco-Lowell, thought that breaking away from the Shops was probably more in the nature of my "being different" and often a "dissenter!" She reminded me of mother's and dad's constant arguments with me about that "different-ness." She added, however, that it was a drive that "came from our parents." They, too, were independent-minded. Also, that it has served me well in becoming a top-ranking student at Thornton and Bates and won me honors in classes and student activities at Bates. "How many," she asked rhetorically "would be able to serve as trainer for eight years of high school and college football? Or with dad's help, rebuild a car between 13 and 15, use the car to help mark the TA football field, earn money for graduate school tuition by serving as both a carpenter and mason, to say nothing about digging and chucking clams for Harvard tuition . . ."

I stopped her with, "Thanks, sister, I didn't realize you were keeping score! But I appreciate your report and confidence". We all laughed as I continued, "Golly I appreciate the cheer leading; Maryllyn, Donna and I are going to need it. But, look, I've 'gotta' split because I want to see a few folk in the shops, then I plan dropping back to see Mark Black for a few moments. You know, I feel that I owe him a special thanks because he's helped keep money flowing into our coffers in all the years since I left Saco- Lowell for Bates in 1939. I'll surely be back by four o'clock or so." With that I went back to my desk to check on the box of stuff to take home, then split for the shops.

In many ways, it was a sentimental journey to see persons from whom I'd asked for and received cooperation. I had wondered and worried how some might react to me, especially when I had to take the side of the Shops and the mechanical engineers while seeming to oppose them. I knew of course that I could not expect to be welcomed or bade farewell with open arms; nevertheless, I felt the urge to try to mend any fences that might still need mending. In fact, I began with Al Calligan who had been called on the carpet by Superintendent Crosby when he became "guilty" of anti-Semitism. As I entered his office, he was on the phone, but motioned me to sit down . . . which I did while he argued with somebody about the dimensions of a particular gear. But the conversation ended rather quickly and Al shook my hand remarking, "I hear that you're going to graduate school at Harvard." I replied in the affirmative and he added, "When I finished at Dartmouth, I had great ambitions to go to MIT, but it didn't happen; I used my experience working summers here plus some correspondence courses when I

231

became foreman. I never thought that those sources helped very much; I had little contact with the teachers." Then, out of the blue, he asked, "Did you ever have any of those courses?"

I responded in the affirmative, "Accounting," and told him that compared with Bates professors, my correspondence "teachers" were nameless and may as well have been working out of a meat locker they were so cold about what I was doing and/or needed. This conversation continued in that vein for 15 or 20 minutes when I told him that I'd come to say "So long" and "Thank you for all the insights and cooperation over the years." I was not quite prepared for what came next. He thanked me for thanking him, then went on to say how sorry he was about his handling the Jewish engineer who seemed to defy him but that the entire incident had made him rethink his biases. He continued with the report that he had made a deliberate effort to talk with Jewish retailers in Saco and Biddeford, had even gone to the Biddeford synagogue to attend a service. He concluded, "Without that encounter with George and the Cost Project, I'd never have taken that opportunity." I was surprised that he actually teared up as he thanked me profusely as he practically whispered his "good-bye."

Naturally, I was on a high after that stop, one that I feared might not be pleasant. Since I was near the Erecting Room and the Ford assembly job, I decided to make a quick stop to see if dad were there as well as Uncle Frank still assembling twisters. As luck would have it, dad was on a late lunch break because he'd been subbing for a person who'd had an accident on the job and had been taken to the infirmary. So we had a little opportunity to catch up on family activity and his own patience in working on the assembly line. He added, "It's heavy work, Roy, but so much more pleasant and do-able than gauging those damned razor-edged Sylvania cans."

"So you're more comfortable than you were? And how are the new doors on the rest room stalls working out? And how's mother?"

"Questions, questions, like old times when you were always asking, "Why? Why? At our garage!""

"Well, dad, never ask questions and you promote ignorance!"

"It's OK, Roy, OK and so is your mother; and she's especially pleased that money is coming in, I'm building my Social Security fund and not simply working on cars for nothing other than '"I-owe-you's!" At that point, he pulled out his thick family-heritage gold watch and said, "I gotta get back to the assembly line or get fired since we're working short-handed today. We're going to see you before you leave for Boston, aren't we?"

"Yup! Will be up Sunday with Maryllyn and Donna. But one more question, dad: 'Is Uncle Frank still working on the twister assembly line?'"

"No, Roy, he's rumored to be in Delaware or somewhere down in that neighborhood directing the assembly of that big Dupont twister order. I think he left last week."

"OK, thanks dad. See you Sunday up at the house."

Continuing my goodbyes, I headed for the Steel Roll and Spindle jobs where I dropped in simply to say "thank you" then headed for the "Automatic Screw Machine" job where it was rumored that they were setting up a newly-designed machine which had "all the bells and whistles." I couldn't stop long but long enough to appreciate what the new machine could do that the old machines would not. At least, I touched bases and collected another eyes-ful of smiles and their warm glows.

I then virtually ran down the five stories to the packing room to say "hello" to my old Umpire Friend, Tubby and say to him, in mock seriousness, "Tubby, I've given up playing base-ball, so will be errorless from now on!"

He tipped his head way back, lifting his right arm as though calling a man out at home plate, and boomed, "Roy, yer *out* and I mean *'out-out'!*" He put out his hand to say, "Good luck! " just as Dan Grady stuck his head through an empty box, yelled "Good luck, Roy," and began singing "Far away and long ago," beckoning Tubby and me to join his Irish voice. Except for us, all was quiet and we looked around to see a circle of fellow-workers and friends who had paused in their hammering although the pungent smell of tar was eye-smarting; they applauded vigorously as we finished. I held out my hand to all who remained in the circle, feeling blessed for both attention and the friendship I'd achieved over my years at the Shops.

Heading for a brief swing through the Saco Plant, I noted an unusually large stack of boxes extending at least fifty feet up the platform beside the railroad siding running parallel to the main track through Biddeford. Curious about the boxes' desti-nation, I walked along side the stacks to note that they were headed for the Dupont plant in Delaware. "Hmmm," I mused, "Uncle Frank is going to have his hands full."

As I headed for the covered bridge to Saco and walked past John Morin's little building which housed Transportation, I tried to spy him, but he was nowhere in sight. I speculated whether or not he would be very pleased to see me anyway, although no doubt glad to see me leave the plant in view of my complaints about his drivers trying to nick me. But I didn't dwell on this, rather headed for John MacScott's office. Here was another potentially tense visit, but I felt a need to speak directly to him and express appreciation for his part in the Pro-ject even if he was nearly driven crazy by Fritz Zimmerman's mode and process of collecting data. Luckily for me, John was alone in his office, extended a strong hand and Scottish brogue greeting that reminded me of the way I was treated as a boy in Saco's Little Scotland in the Common-Bartlett-Middle Street sections of Saco, sometimes called "Little Scotland."

John didn't seem too busy; at least his desk was not piled very high with papers and blueprints, as I'd seen it many times during my initiation year in the Summer of 1936. As always, he was very direct in speaking of Fritz Zimmerman: "You know, Roy, I came to appreciate the man after I got to know him better. After we'd met for dinner and I'd explored his machine for planing propellers for ocean-going ships, I had a true admiration for him. Anybody that smart and meticulous could not be all bad, and I gradually got used to seeing and experiencing him as a real and helpful person. I still couldn't get used to his tiny printing and hand-writing; but, then, I wasn't there to rate him on penmanship. So I eventually accepted his thoroughness and figured if you and your staff over at the office found him to be OK, then it was OK with me. Also despite my Presbyterian heritage, I accepted him as a Jew; and, I guess he accepted me as a tried and true (sometimes blue!) Scotsman!"

These comments were music to my ears. I expressed appreciation for John's cooperation, explained a bit of where and why I was going to graduate school in the hope that I might become a college or university professor. In his own way, John wished me "good fortune," put his arm around my shoulders as he escorted me toward the Paint Department where he knew I would say good-bye to Woody.

As usual Woody was donned in what I'd come to call his "space suit," so John suggested that I stand back a safe distance or go upstairs to see Superintendent Loranger as I had first intended. So when Woody waved, I pointed upstairs and he nodded as understanding my intentions.

When I reached the second floor and in sight of Loranger's Office, I could see that he had somebody with him, but I couldn't see "Who?" Walking closer, I saw that it was my old TA classmate, Phil Glaude. Loranger beckoned me to come in.

"I'd heard you were coming," Loranger said. "Mark Black called to say that he'll see you at 4 o'clock." Seeing that it was now 3:15, I shook hands with Phil, sat down for a moment until they finished their discussion about some shop form or other. But as Phil stood to leave, Loranger beckoned him to sit down for a moment, then added, "I want for us to tell Roy about our reaction to the Cost Project and for him to know that while we were skeptical about its success in the beginning, we want to hand him accolades for the spirit in which he directed it and faced all the diversity and adversity that this company knows. Phil, please tell him what you think and why!"

For many years I had perceived Phil as a relatively slow and cautious fellow but a clear thinker, hence I was not surprised when he cleared his throat a bit and began, "As you know, Mr. Loranger, I've known Roy since grade school. He always worked hard and got high grades, but also knew how to work with his hands (as in Manual Training under Charlie Clark or in his father's garage.) In fact, I know his father, too, and Roy's a chip off the old block. I, too, wondered if this Cost Project could work even though I knew that Mr. Kettley had thought it through before his brilliant conception and strong determination to do it. When I heard that Roy had been chosen to direct it, I knew it was going to be a difficult task but I thought that Roy had the "tools" to do it and did what I could to assist. Since Roy knows how to evaluate events and actions by using academic letters, I award him an 'A-minus' for his job."

"Why minus?" Loranger scowled and asked, aloud, while I filed his question in my memory!

Phil was prompt to respond. "Because nobody's perfect," he said, clearly, then in a jovial mode he said, "also and furthermore, he's leaving us to go to graduate school in an entirely different field."

Loranger then laughed heartily, "But, Phil, you could have made it 'A+' because we could always have wiped out the plus!"

Then we all laughed and I observed, "It's OK, Phil, I'll take whatever I can get! And it may give me a different attitude regarding achievement of perfection!" As we backed through Loranger's office door, he said, "Wait a minute," held out his hand and said, "Incidentally, thanks for urging us to take on John Morin for his managing the vehicles that do in-shop delivery. As you may know, he's on 'probation' for a year. This is not for public announcement, but I thought you might want to know how important it was that you called it to our attention. Phil may tell you more."

On that note, I went out with Phil, getting more details about Morin's 'probation' and with the intention of stopping only a moment with Woody before walking across the bridge with Phil and get to Mark Black's office by four o'clock. And that we did! Woody was out of his space suit. Phil also knew him and we shook hands all around and I told him that I'd plan to see him at his home sometime since he was one of mother's and dad's friends and neighbors. Then Phil and I strolled across the covered bridge leisurely, chatting about old times and our families. As we split for his office and mine, I said, "See you tomorrow in the funny papers or at least at our 10th or 25th TA Reunion." It was a genial parting.

I reached Black's office at just 4 o'clock, knocked, went in. His first words: "Do you think we should pay you for today's good will tour?" I laughed. Then we laughed together and he added, "just kidding!"

237

"I hope so because I can use every dollar I can coral, but do as you wish! It's been a very reaffirming day for me. And I think that some of the ruffled feathers over ethnicity may have been smoothed down more than I'd hoped. Both Al Calligan in the Gear Job and John MacScott across the River seem to have learned something from their unusual ethnic encounter. I also found a fairly good reaction to the engineers as well as the project in general."

"That doesn't surprise me. What you do not know relates to an informal poll that your old classmate, Phil Glaude, took among both foremen and second hands. You got almost 100% approval though the entire shop."

"Strange, Mark, and I hope I may call you 'Mark' from this day forward?"

"Of course, Roy, and I hope you'll visit me occasionally at home as the years go by. . . ."

"Thank you, I shall . . . but as I started to say, I just came from Loranger's office where Phil happened to be, and he didn't say a word about it!"

"He was asked not to," Mark smiled.

"Nor was he permitted to share another piece of good news. Mr. Kettley is attempting to get the S-L-S Corporate board to approve a $1000 bonus for your outstanding effort on behalf of Saco-Lowell, even though we wish you were staying on to become a member of our management team! What's more, he is trying to push the idea of a two-pronged scholarship program to expand our own Apprenticeship Program as well as offer modest grants (which will be competitive) to those who wish to further their education in any field, business, science or the arts.

"When or if Kettley gets approval of this rather unusual approach to encourage education, we'll run your photo in the local newspapers and will send the announcement to Bates via

Harry Rowe, the dean who managed to get the faculty to release you in December, 1942 to help us with the Ford carriage wheel job. I shall not soon forget my interchange with Dean Rowe and the faculty decision at a tough time in our nation's history. He was very flexible and understanding. But he knew whom he was recommending . . . as did I."

I thanked Mark Black for the honor and congratulated him, Kettley and the corporate powers for their forward-looking contribution to their employees' futures.

I said good-bye to him, waived farewell to all my old friends down through the two departments with which I had been associated in various ways over a period of more than eight years.

Back at the office, I talked further with Grace and Priscilla about my "tour" of the various departments, shared with them Mark Black's news of a possible nod to the importance of education. In those closing moments, I thanked them as well as other members of the Cost Project, gave each a hug. My last good-bye went to Charlie Crogan with the observation: "Charlie, I commend you for your loyalty to the Yankees, but someday let's go to Fenway Park together so I can help you find the advantages of becoming a Red Sox fan."

EPILOGUE

The Saco-Lowell Shops applied for and received the needed relief from frozen labor and materials rates; they remained in business in Biddeford and Saco until 1957 when they moved lock, stock and spindle to Easley, S.C., with many of their key personnel living in Greensboro, N.C.

The design changes mentioned in Chapter 31 continued to be made in rapid succession until the steps in the number of processes were reduced in number to resemble line-production techniques of most products of US industry. Naturally, this included new metals, plastics and automation aided via electronics and laser technology as predicted by earlier Saco-Lowell engineers.

It is difficult to follow their corporate history. As early as 1952, S-L-S joined the Post-WWII diversification processes when constructing a modern building on North Street in Saco (named for David Edwards) which eventually produced machine guns for the U.S. Defense Department although it first made automobile parts for Maremont Corporation. As I learned in the late Eighties via an interviewing tour of a dozen or so former Biddeford and Saco key persons living in the Easley and Greensboro area. The Easley operation had already extended to England, Spain and other parts of the South and were owned at the minimum by Platt, Maremont and Hollingsworth. In fact it might require a corporate lawyer to follow that trail or pattern. Those interested in lawsuits may wish to follow the fine print via the Internet.

Meanwhile the Saco & Biddeford plants have undergone various modifications via fire and demolition, creating condos by reconstructing the interiors of some of the buildings. Private owners are now landlords of thousands of square feet rented by artists, craftsmen, entrepreneurs and office workers. The corrugated bridge, which figures prominently in my story and which literally tied the Saco & Biddeford plants together, is no longer in place. But the external appearance of the massive brick buildings is much as it was when early postal-card makers were pointing their cameras up river from the bridge connecting York and Dean's Hills. (See photos.) The local brickyards, which poured millions upon millions of their products into both corporate and public economies have closed their yards long since. But the very existence of the massive buildings is symbolic of the work force as an engine that made the local economy teeter between evident prosperity and the ever-present concern that the corporations would "move South" or run out of ingenuity to support the cotton textile industry.

Following Sanford's example to be the "town that would never die," both cities began a new era by investing energy and ingenuity to build Industrial Parks, mostly in the suburbs and not downtown.

BIBLIOGRAPHY

The most comprehensive history of Saco-Lowell is George Sweet Gibb's *The Saco–Lowell Shops: Textile Machinery in New England, 1813–1949* (Cambridge, Harvard University Press, 1950). This study, No. XVI of the Harvard Studies in Business History, unfortunately stopped just short of Saco-Lowell's beginning the sell-out or diversification process as well as the major physical move from Biddeford–Saco to the South. Many of its records joined previous ones at the Baker Library at Harvard Business School.

One of the most interesting sections of Gibb's book, for my purposes, consists of Chapter XIV, "The Hard Climb Back, 1926–1941" in which Gibb analyzes the consolidation that took place under the direction of President David F. Edward, located in Boston, and his two major colleagues, VP R. A. Kettley and A. V. Stuart, located in Saco–Biddeford. In that connection, Appendix 16, Edward's December 15, 1927, "Report on Plant Consolidation" (pp. 685–700) to the corporate Board, is central to the mission of our special cost project. This is verifiable fact, no part of the fiction in which I indulged.

PHOTOS & COMPANY HISTORY

When my editor, Tom Laga, critiqued and corrected this manuscript, he occasionally ran into passages wherein the technical language got in the way of clarity. Hence, in choosing a few photos and diagrams, I decided to let the photos explain themselves at a couple of critical points. First, there is the overview of the Biddeford Plant where at the lower right-hand corner one may see the white corrugated iron bridge spanning the river to connect Saco and Biddeford which I mention at various times in the text to give geographical locations (*image A, below*).

IMAGE A

Then, since the major function of cotton textile machines, is historically, to run the decreasingly smaller threads between rolls turning at various speeds (stretching and twisting them), then wind them on bobbins which eventually reach the loom, some pictures and diagrams catch that process/drama (*images B, this page; C, opposite page; D, page 246*). Using a Lubrication Diagram catches the complexity of gear heads on most machines where fine adjustments can be made to help control the process (*image E, page 247*). Finally, the photos of banks of carding and roving machines reflect some sense of a typical mill with its multiplicity and adjacency of machines (*image F, page 248*).

IMAGE B

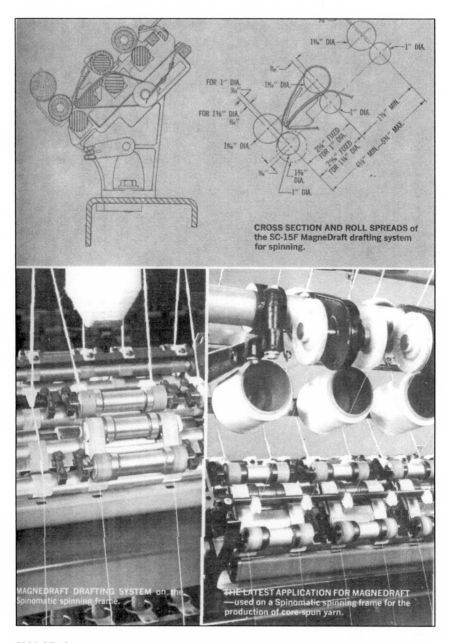

CROSS SECTION AND ROLL SPREADS of the SC-15F MagneDraft drafting system for spinning.

MAGNEDRAFT DRAFTING SYSTEM on the Spinomatic spinning frame.

THE LATEST APPLICATION FOR MAGNEDRAFT —used on a Spinomatic spinning frame for the production of core-spun yarn.

IMAGE C

IMAGE D

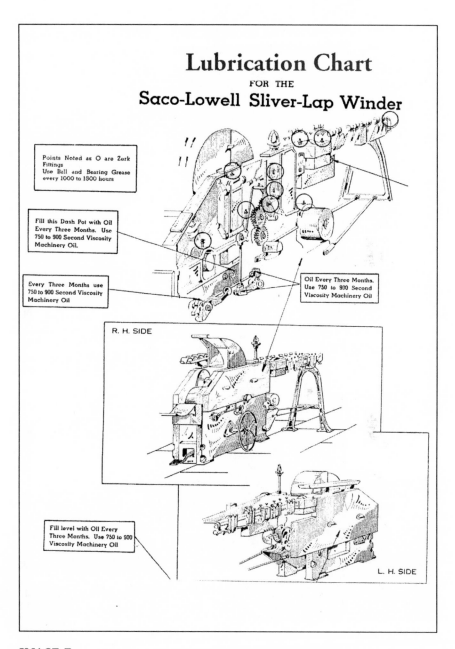

Lubrication Chart
FOR THE
Saco-Lowell Sliver-Lap Winder

Points Noted as O are Zerk Fittings
Use Ball and Bearing Grease every 1000 to 1500 hours

Fill this Dash Pot with Oil Every Three Months. Use 750 to 900 Second Viscosity Machinery Oil.

Every Three Months use 750 to 900 Second Viscosity Machinery Oil

Oil Every Three Months. Use 750 to 900 Second Viscosity Machinery Oil

R. H. SIDE

Fill level with Oil Every Three Months. Use 750 to 900 Viscosity Machinery Oil

L. H. SIDE

IMAGE E

247

IMAGE F

LARGE COMPANIES IN SACO & BIDDEFORD,
1811-1945[1]

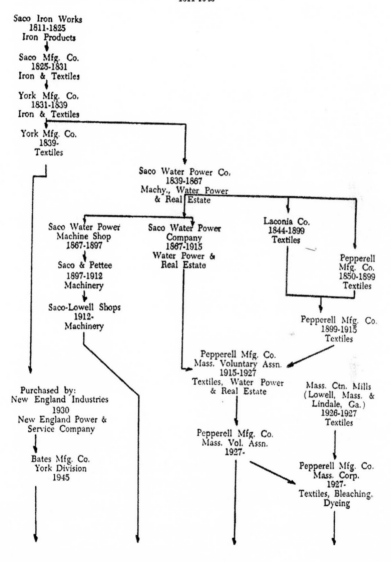

Saco Iron Works
1811-1825
Iron Products

Saco Mfg. Co.
1825-1831
Iron & Textiles

York Mfg. Co.
1831-1839
Iron & Textiles

York Mfg. Co.
1839-
Textiles

Saco Water Power Co.
1839-1867
Machy., Water Power
& Real Estate

Saco Water Power
Machine Shop
1867-1897

Saco & Pettee
1897-1912
Machinery

Saco-Lowell Shops
1912-
Machinery

Saco Water Power
Company
1867-1915
Water Power &
Real Estate

Laconia Co.
1844-1899
Textiles

Pepperell
Mfg. Co.
1850-1899
Textiles

Pepperell Mfg. Co.
1899-1915
Textiles

Pepperell Mfg. Co.
Mass. Voluntary Assn.
1915-1927
Textiles, Water Power
& Real Estate

Purchased by:
New England Industries
1930
New England Power &
Service Company

Bates Mfg. Co.
York Division
1945

Pepperell Mfg. Co.
Mass. Vol. Assn.
1927-

Mass. Ctn. Mills
(Lowell, Mass. &
Lindale, Ga.)
1926-1927
Textiles

Pepperell Mfg. Co.
Mass. Corp.
1927-
Textiles, Bleaching,
Dyeing

1. Adapted from Evelyn H. Knowlton, *Pepperell's Progress*,
8, by permission of Harvard University Press.

IMAGES OF THE SACO-LOWELL SHOPS

Breinigsville, PA USA
08 October 2009
225517BV00002B/4/P